Deviancy

Rose Linderman

Rose Linderman, Psy.D.

DEVIANCY
Published by Bar Code Graphics
Gulfport, Florida

ISBN: 978-0-578-34958-9
TRUE CRIME / Forensics

Cover and Interior Design by Victoria Wolf, wolfdesignandmarketing.com.
Copyright owned by Rose Linderman Psy. D.

This story includes a fictional thriller in combination with actual forensic case evaluations that have been altered to protect the individuals' actual identities. Cases involve the character of Dr. Susan Kasson, who in real life is the author, Dr. Rose Linderman, Psy.D., a forensic psychologist. Any resemblance of these true cases shared with the reader to actual persons, living or dead, or historical events is purely coincidental.

"Though a good deal is too strange to believe, nothing is too strange to not have happened."

—Thomas Hardy 1840–1928

Contents

Author's Note

Assessing mental illness in an individual facing possible criminal prosecution involves making sense of the person's current level of intelligence, general life history, past sanctions, adaptability to generally expected rules of social conduct, and current level of risk of harm to themselves and others. Also important is the current assessment and understanding of the individual's candor in participating in a psychological evaluation related to issues of possible confinement or serious sanction.

The evaluations offering the best opinions include a review of a variety of pertinent records within a specific and noted period of time, with noted inconsistencies or differences, if such exist.

Potentially severe penalties for certain acts can influence candor in the interviewee. As such, follow-up interviews and cross-checking information across time may clarify differences in responses in combination with a careful and detailed review of pertinent records.

Prelude

This story begins as historical fiction, with vignettes of true forensic cases with the actual identities of all subjects protected, as detailed by the character of Dr. Susan Kasson.

In reality, the author of this book, Dr. Linderman, is acutely aware and familiar with criminality and mental illness. She has served as a forensic psychologist over three decades of time, performed civil and criminal psychological evaluations, served as an expert witness, and testified in a variety of cases involving individuals familiar with violence and acts of harm toward others.

If you asked Dr. Linderman if she ever felt fear around the people she interviewed, she would say she never took reckless chances. Before she interviewed any of the people she was court ordered to evaluate, she reviewed their life and legal histories, details of their behaviors, history of their crimes, and psychiatric records. And she asked jail or prison staff of any recently known abrupt behavior issues in the individual she was about to meet and interview.

There were times when she opted to sit on a chair outside the person's jail cell to conduct her interview. In all cases, she was aware that staff were able to observe both her and the person she was interviewing on closed circuit television.

On occasion she asked her questions to the incarcerated or hospitalized defendant over a telephone while observing them from behind thick impact-resistant glass. And then there were the interviews where the respondent's attorney was present as well as others related to a pending court case involving the possibility of indeterminant commitment.

She had only been attacked once, despite the presence of two attending staff flanking the patient who was walking in a circle in the padded room of a hospital psychiatric ward, singing the alphabet song in the voice of a child.

In a lightning fast lucky grab of hair, one of Dr. Linderman's fingers was bent, but not broken, in her attempt to block the woman's sudden lunge.

It was a lesson never forgotten. The number one rule is to stay safe and learn. Rule two is to be aware of your surroundings and never ever ignore or suppress your sense that something is wrong, off, out of order, strange, or not right.

When you sense fear, move to a safer place.

Listen to your inner alarms.

Be vigilant.

Never forget these guidelines.

Chapter 1

Clouds blacked out the moonlight. Thunder, flashes of lightening, and a blinding downpour accompanied Anne Tolbar, RN, as she drove home from her evening shift just past midnight.

As she rounded the curve to her personal parking area, she saw through the rain spattered windshield what appeared to be a man lowering a body into the back of his van. She quickly dismissed this crazy thought as due to her being extremely tired.

She pulled into her designated parking space, turned off her car, and gathered her purse and sweater. Suddenly the man came running over, waving his arms, and calling out to her. She recognized him as Lewis Weller, a fellow who occasionally cleaned her carpet.

Earlier in the evening, Lewis was cleaning carpets in the home of Anne's neighbor, Joan Frye, when he commented that he liked the painting covering a hidden wall safe in the den. He volunteered he was aware there was a hidden safe behind the painting because he used to work at a site where such pieces were fabricated, and he had installed both the safes and the artwork camouflaging them.

Joan immediately informed Mr. Weller that she was going to call the guard to come and escort him off the premises. A struggle ensued; Lewis was the victor. Joan Frye was the first recipient of the chloroform-soaked cloth. The colorless, volatile, and sweet-smelling liquid quickly rendered her unconscious.

Lewis astutely removed his business card from her kitchen calendar, which noted his name and phone number. When he heard Anne arriving home, he emerged from behind his parked van, waving his arms and calling out, "Stop, help me ... she started seizing ... I can get her to the ER faster than waiting for an ambulance! Help me please!"

As he darted to open Anne's car door, he pleaded, "We have to hurry! Help! We can save her!"

Anne jumped out of her car, her right hand still holding her cell phone. But before she could open her mouth to ask a single question, her face was the second to be covered with the chloroform-soaked cloth, and a hood was pulled over her head to hold the cloth close to her face. That was how her evening and her life ended.

She never felt her body being placed next to that of her neighbor. She would never fully know what she was dealing with. She had never died before.

And somewhere in the distance, an owl could be heard softly hooting. An omen of death.

Chapter 2

Lewis Weller was a tall, handsome man in his early forties, physically fit, verbally facile almost to a fault, and single. He was intelligent and had a college degree that few of his friends even knew about. His previous employment included a pharmaceutical firm, a fact known only by potential employers who had access to his personal information. Currently, he was a foreman at Lake Crest Cemetery where he was in charge of a crew of twenty men—a job he had held for greater than the past decade.

The men liked and trusted him; they said he was a competent and fair boss and a pro at training the workers to do a variety of tasks. They commented on his skill at showing them shortcuts for ways to do a quality job or fix something that was broken.

More to the point, he was a calculated planner and thinker. He was also gifted at disappearing at exactly the right moment to avoid detection in the midst of personal trouble or conflict. Curiously, people in need of his special talents recognized his dark side.

Like many a psychopath, Lewis exuded superficial charm and a distaste for boredom. He felt no remorse. He had no evidence of even a muted sense of responsibility, guilt, or empathy. And he was criminally versatile.

Lewis's story begins in the United States. No one knows his current location. Hopefully, it is nowhere near you.

Chapter 3

Five funerals were slated for Tuesday at Foxx Brothers Funeral Home, located on the sprawling, emerald green hillside of Lake Crest Cemetery. Three funerals were for elderly individuals who had lived long and prosperous lives. One was for an infant, and one was for Henri Muller, a local founding father of a successful bridge engineering firm that bore his name.

Staff at Foxx Brothers gave all their guests the utmost attention and care. But, Mr. Muller required even more finesse due to the large crowd expected to attend the memorial of his life's work and many successes. Not to underscore the fact that Henri long ago planned his own funeral, beginning with his choice of the National Solid Seamless Copper Deposit Casket, sales price $35,000.

Henri was elderly and physically frail. By contrast, his casket was not only expensive, but heavy, weighing over 600 pounds. The challenges accompanying this burial unit were mitigated by a quietly motorized, remote control church truck that moved the massive coffin effortlessly down any aisle or hallway.

Henri had been a major contributor to the local arts community. He donated land to the city and constructed bridges connecting vast waterways and land masses throughout the state. His life and his departure from earth needed to be grand and memorable.

Extended family members from far and wide would be at his funeral, filling the Episcopal cathedral to capacity. Those present would listen to readings and music specifically chosen or requested by Henri. In all, there would be a variety of choirs, soloists, and orchestral selections.

Henri had requested that four dozen apricot-colored roses adorn the hood of his copper coffin. He had carefully planned the seating order of people invited to his funeral to evidence his gratitude for their special level of importance to him. If guests complained of their seating order, directions had been left to inform them that the list was Henri's idea; if too much protestation occurred, they were to be shown the list bearing their names under the headings *Specific Seating* versus *General Seating*. Copies of these plans had been given to his attorney and most trusted board member to ensure everything ran smoothly on this most significant day of remembrance.

Extra staff were required to manage the earlier private ceremony for immediate family prior to the public review. Additional help was necessary to park cars and collect and mark memorial gifts as well as load, transport, unload, and arrange the many floral displays at the cathedral, keeping in mind that certain florals were to be more prominently displayed.

A police escort would lead the limousines bearing family members first to the cathedral and then back to Lake Crest Cemetery, where a limited number of close friends would participate in speaking prior to Henri's casket being moved to his marble mausoleum. Following the service, a private party to celebrate Henri's philanthropic life would be held at the Muller estate for an expected 200 guests.

Chapter 4

Seth Loring, one of the lead funeral directors at Foxx Brothers, part of the expansive Lake Crest Cemetery Complex, was in charge of Henri's massive extravaganza. He had organized and reviewed all procedures with the regular and added staff, so there would be no glitches.

Seth was an attractive man, a princely 6'2" with sandy colored hair, the physique of an athlete, and eyes bluer that those of Paul Newman. He was savvy, organized, articulate, socially aware, and sensitive.

Apart from his quiet and professional demeanor at the funeral home, Seth was a caring custodian of a younger brother, Sam, who lived with him due to a brain injury acquired while serving as a Marine in Afghanistan. When Sam was not at the VA hospital receiving treatment, he performed odd jobs at Foxx Brothers, like keeping the hearses immaculately clean and assisting with the maintenance of flower beds and shrubbery nearest the large, ornate funeral home. Sam could do everything but drive a vehicle.

Foxx Brothers supported their funeral directors being visible in the community, knowing these positive connections could, and did, pay off. As such, Seth belonged to an array of community organizations, played cello in the local symphony, and was known for helping with fundraising in community events and civic organizations.

Everyone at Foxx Brothers was expected, at all times and especially during big events such as the Muller funeral, to be impeccably dressed, pressed, polished, and alert to the responsibilities of their respective positions.

The male funeral directors wore dark navy suits, light blue shirts, and navy ties with a deep purple abstract pattern. Women directors also wore dark navy suits, light blue silk blouses, and a neck scarf bearing the same purple pattern as the ties of their male counterparts.

All directors had the same taupe-colored raincoats with black arm bands and water-resistant black hats. All Foxx Funeral Home attire had employees' names embroidered on the collars so as to not be mistaken for those of mourners. Foxx Brothers thrived on details and funerals running smoothly.

Chapter 5

The day prior to the ceremony, Seth turned on a favorite classical music station and began his careful and fastidious process of preparing and embalming Henri for his last and final public reviewal.

Seth was a master in arterial and chemistry skills. He could mix the perfect combination of humectant, dye, preservatives, and germicides for any situation, whether it was an uncomplicated embalming, a long-refrigerated body with gangrene or postmortem staining, a body that had sustained traumatic injury or was partly decomposed, or one having an extended history of heavy medication.

He was known for his ability to take whatever challenge he was presented and make it turn out well. His colleagues called him with their worst nightmares and shared descriptions of his greatest feats.

Henri's body was first bathed with a disinfectant solution, then his limbs were massaged and manipulated to relieve rigor mortis. Next, Seth set Henri's jaw, closed and capped the eyelids, and shaped the mouth into a pleasant and relaxed smile.

He combined the formaldehyde, glutaraldehyde, methanol, ethanol, phenol, and water along with a perfect mixture of dyes to make Henri as genteel appearing in death as he had been in his successful life. Seth fastidiously monitored the Dodge Embalming Machine, attending to how Henri's body was responding to the process. Periodically, he would massage Henri's limbs, especially the fingers and fingertips, to work the embalming fluid evenly into all anatomical nooks and crannies.

He posed Henri's right hand to enable it to hold the large, ornate, and hand-carved Meerschaum pipe that Henri would take with him to the next world. Occasionally he squeezed the back of the wrist to observe the embalming progress.

Then Henri was carefully bathed, packed, clothed, and lowered by lift into the National.

Lastly, Seth began his last feats of cosmetic magic, transforming Henri into as dapper a man as he had been in life: smooth shaven, tanned, slightly smiling, and sporting a perfectly trimmed full moustache accented by softly brushed hair.

This was Henri's last white tie event, and he looked it right down to the apricot rose and emerald green fern in the lapel of his tux.

Standing back and looking at Henri, Seth's first words were, "This man looks like he is about to be swallowed by the National! We have to fix this." He called for the help of David, an assisting director, and together they lifted Henri enough to place an extra foam pad under the body, raising him higher in the bed of the coffin.

"Now this looks much better," said David. "Henri definitely looked as though he was being consumed. Not surprising … he must only weigh 140 pounds soaking wet. Great job, Seth."

For the finishing touch, white velvet folds of cloth surrounding Henri's head were carefully arranged. Everything had been done to his requests. Henri looked dignified, refined, and peaceful.

"Man, this is a fantastic presentation, Seth. I have never seen such elegance … or such expense!" They both smiled a knowing smile. As other directors passed by, they also looked in and offered praise for the final presentation of Mr. Henri Muller.

Sadly, and unbeknown to Seth, was the dastardly fact that Henri was not alone in the impressive National on his way to meet God!

Hidden beneath Henri's body, appearing to be merely a black rubberized mattress adding comfort for the deceased, was tiny Anne Tolbar, solidly frozen, wrapped in heavy plastic, and secretly placed within the under portion of the massive coffin. The woman's body had been hidden after the National was wiped down and readied to be taken to the mortuary from the product receiving area, an annex next to the crematorium.

Chapter 6

After the ceremony, Seth conducted the usual debriefing with the staff. "How did we do on the Muller funeral?" he asked the group of two dozen professionals sitting around the conference table before him. "What, if anything, went wrong, and what can we do to change it in the future?"

The staff members relayed the varied and complimentary comments shared by the attending guests. One woman had asked, "Are all funerals at Foxx this elegant?" which caused a ripple of soft laughter. No one brought up problems because basically, or so everyone thought, there had been none.

Newspaper accounts of the funeral were profusely positive, and a week later when handwritten letters of appreciation by Henri's family and his board of directors were received, they were posted for all to read. Seth was generous in his remarks to the staff as to how they made a huge event run smoothly. And why shouldn't he have been? The Muller funeral paralleled a theatrical production that had gone off more magnificently than anyone could imagine, even Henri himself.

Chapter 7

Rockford City, population 350,000, was home of the Lake Crest Cemetery Complex and included not only the Foxx Brothers Funeral Home, but also a vast array of gardens and tree lined drives, as well as the Lake Crest Crematorium.

The city itself was in the eastern portion of the Midwest River Valley, surrounded by limestone bluffs and hillsides covered with dark, emerald green pines amidst an array of deciduous trees more noticeable in the autumn with their vibrant fall colors. Rocky bluffs of tan and white stone highlighted the visual contrasts.

The city itself boasted varied business entities, financial institutions, two universities, and an active cultural center that featured opera, theater, and a variety of special guest entertainers. The city was a hub for a number of major airlines that offered direct flights to Europe and Asia.

Rockford City also included a large granite mining firm, a major medical center complex that served people from surrounding states, and a population that had demonstrated consistent growth over time.

Lake Crest itself consisted of thousands of graves dating back to the 1800s, an eye-catching vista of ornate statuary and tombstones, manicured floral gardens, an array of fountains, and areas for visitors to sit and contemplate the meaning of life.

Some of the earliest headstones—whose names and dates were still decipherable—noted births dating back to the 1700s. If you stood on the patio off the back of the Lake Crest Funeral Home, you could capture the panoramic beauty of the rolling landscape dotted with its thousands of gravestones and winding roadways. When visitors walked onto the patio for the first time, it was common to hear, "This is quite a view. ... You can see forever, from here. ... It is amazingly beautiful."

Susan Kasson, Psy. D. felt the same about the vista and the area as a whole, which is why she had established her forensic psychology practice in the city fifteen years prior. The central location connected her with the surrounding cities and institutions where she regularly drove for court ordered evaluations.

She was in her midforties, tall, personable, and fairly attractive. She had served as a court examiner for civil and criminal cases for a number of years, assessing individuals to determine their competency to stand trial and/or their mental status at the time of the offense. The results and findings of her evaluations could result in an individual being determined insane or unable to realize the nature of their crime or that their actions were wrong.

Common to others in her profession, these cases included a review of extensive police and arrest records, court transcripts, personal and criminal histories, and ultimately meeting and interviewing individuals in various prisons, jails, or state hospitals.

These interviews included a line of questioning to assess respondents' competency to proceed to trial or capacity for change. The questions also determined if the respondents met the statutory criteria as competent or incompetent to stand trial, mentally ill and dangerous, that of a sexually dangerous person/sexual psychopathic personality, or other designation as ordered by the court. Based on her assessments, some individuals were civilly committed indefinitely to state hospital forensic units.

Most all of the people Susan interviewed had long histories of mental illness, crime, confinements that netted no changes in their behaviors, and repeat offenses that eventually added to their determination of being seen as dangerous. A thorough review of each case prior to actually meeting the respondent in person was the bedrock of her case conceptualization.

During her review of records, she took extensive notes and listed specific questions—including inconsistencies that needed clearing up by the individual when they met in person. This would help Susan understand the individual's thinking and actions at the time of the offense.

The people she interviewed were informed that her purpose in talking with them was ordered by the court in the county in which they resided. They had the right to decline the interview, and some did, as though not understanding that the records of their patterns of behavior spoke for them. At least participating in an interview could give them a chance to tell their version of what happened and ask questions about what was ahead for them.

During the interviews, Susan introduced herself, explained the limits of confidentiality related to the case, and clarified the individual's right to ask questions when they did not understand certain words or the reasons for the questions being asked by the court.

Evaluations typically lasted from two to three hours, the difference related to the individual case and whether the person agreed to be

interviewed. If someone declined the interview, the reported conclusion would be based solely on the massive content contained within
the records, which she would note in her report to the court.

Chapter 8

The last remaining entity in the sprawling Lake Crest complex was the crematorium, under the meticulous management of Milton Beardsley, a lifelong Rockford City denizen who talked like he had known just about everyone buried in the cemetery—their most admirable qualities and particularly, their faults.

The crematorium sat at the end of a slightly winding road, bordered by trees and additional gardens with the commonly available benches for visitors.

Milton Beardsley had managed the crematorium for over three decades. He was a bastion of knowledge related to who was buried, where (and the reason, if it involved a good story), why they were important, and the exact location of their place of final rest. This knowledge was due to his having created an extensive mapping of the cemetery, so visitors could more easily find family graves among the sea of headstones.

Milton also shared the responsibilities of the cemetery grounds. To say he ran a tight ship would be an understatement; he was more of a cranky perfectionist. He was adamant that all tools be cleaned before being put away, any dirt washed off all surfaces, and everything be replaced in its designated spot.

He often vented his suspicions and frustrations about the lack of work-motivated youth with his cohort, Lloyd Barclay, over coffee at the crematorium office. Lloyd and Milton had been friends for years, and knowing more than most, loved to share many a laugh about their white-collar bosses, who, in their opinions, knew less than they collectively had forgotten.

Milton had recently weakened and given his sister's son, Chadly, a job on the grave digging crew. Problem was, Milton and most other grounds crew workers considered Chadly's employment as solely related to his being family, not because he was a gifted or hard worker, let alone smart.

Milton described the boy as having a "brain like a sieve, unable to walk and chew gum at the same time." The other workers resented Chadly's employment and assessed him as being basically "a lazy dumb-ass," which caused Milton to respond, "What laser like insight … you think this is news?"

Lloyd sipped his coffee before commenting, "Your sister will be pissed if the boy gets canned, but the other guys in the excavating crew will probably be relieved. Chad has been a real drag. Usually when I see him with the crew, they are talking to each other like he is not even there. He needs a solitary job like floor polishing in a mall, or some kind of robot job he can do alone."

"Yep, I know what you mean, Lloyd. Say, before you get back to work, I gotta show you the neatest thing I got out of the ovens." Milton stood up and walked briskly to a box in the corner of the room.

He then held up something metal and smiled, "Look at this baby," he said, "It's somebody's hip replacement, untouched by the heat and just laying amidst the cremains. I can't decide whether to add it to my collection of treasures, make a putter out of it, or save it until I need a new hip myself. If I did that, I would have to golf alone, so as not to offend anyone. Everyone I golfed with would think it could be from someone they knew. Isn't it neat?"

"Hey, it's great, Milt. It will be a fantastic addition to your collection. Perhaps it's an omen of good luck … maybe during your upcoming fishing trip, you will actually catch something we can eat … God knows I have heard enough of your fish stories." They laughed and slapped each other on the back. Milton jumped in his truck and headed down the service road.

Chapter 9

The next evening on his way out of town, Milton Beardsley gave into his growing concerns, if not suspicions, about Chadly and took a side road into Lake Crest. He parked off the service road near the east utility shed, stooped under the massive gate barrier, and walked toward the tool shed. He was sure equipment would be left out because Chadly was still working with the crew when Milton left for home, and it would have been his nephew's job to clean the tools and put them back in order.

The night was dark and quiet. The only sounds were the call of a distant great horned owl somewhere in the night along with the reply from its mate.

Milton's footsteps crunched on the crushed rock path strewn with pine cones. At night, Lake Crest could become a surreal experience of obsidian shadows mixed with the speckled lighting from the huge ornate lampposts that lit the grand drives.

Usually, no one witnessed this perspective or commented about it because there were no public visitors at night, nor was there a security staff. The eerie experience was accentuated by the shadows cast by the huge headstones, as though the deceased of decades past reigned supreme.

Milton was thinking about a lot of things when he suddenly came face to face with an unrecognizable, dark clothed figure standing under the shadow of a large tree.

Neither person was expecting any distractions, let alone meeting anyone, in this place at this time of night. But one of them was more alert.

Milton was completely consumed by catching his nephew having left tools uncleaned and laying around. He was caught off guard. In just seconds, a shovel edge split his head, ultimately killing him. He never had time to recognize the stranger, let alone question the reason he might be present on a dark path in the cemetery at this time of night.

Milton's last words were, "Who the hell … ?" followed by shooting pain, unconsciousness, and then, death. Both men were on separate, secret, and vastly unrelated missions. Milton had the most to lose.

Never in a million years would Milton have guessed that the day he was supposed to leave for his annual fishing bonanza would be the last one of his life.

Also unimagined was his being bludgeoned to death by one of the tools he oversaw others working with every day. And lastly, his being covered with a common white sheet, wrapped in plastic, placed in an Elderlight heavy cardboard coffin, and put in the crematory refrigerated room with a note attached that read, "County John Doe. Paperwork will be sent electronically. Thanks." The signature was illegible, as were areas requiring initials. Everything looked official. Just another pauper.

And his killer, well, that would be Lewis Weller who deftly picked the lock of the crematory door and rolled Milton into the building. Nothing looked or seemed out of order.

The bigger question was, what was Lewis Weller doing at the cemetery after hours with a shovel in hand, and what did he have to hide?

Twenty-four hours later, following the customary holding time for any/all bodies scheduled for cremation, the cardboard container bearing Milton Beardsley's corporeal form moved slowly along the conveyor belt. The oven doors opened. The boxed body entered the retort; the doors slowly closed. The burners ignited. The cremation began.

Five hours later, Milton's cremains were carefully swept together with a small brush, then placed in a box, dated, labeled as "John Doe," and placed in the area marked "HOLDING/TO BE PICKED UP."

Lake Crest would never be the same.

Chapter 10

Susan heard about Milton Beardsley's accident on the morning radio news as she was driving to an evaluation. Everyone in the county knew the Beardsley family. News of Milton's death was shocking and left a lot of folks confused. Milton's nephew, who especially adored his uncle, was inconsolable.

Also in the news was an update of the sexual assault case in which Susan was involved. The radio announcer reported the "young woman had nearly been killed after being held captive for four days in a man's house." The man, Mark Backstrom, had been found guilty of First Degree Assault, First Degree Criminal Sexual Conduct, and Kidnapping. The newscaster described him as being "led out of jail in shackles." Little was said about the young woman who was his victim and a survivor beyond all odds.

Susan evaluated Mark Backstrom for two and one-half hours. Ultimately, based on his history and the additional recent assault, she recommended he be adjudicated a Patterned Sex Offender, which put him in line for a markedly longer sentence.

She recommended confinement based on Mr. Backstrom's history and demonstrated lack of remorse, compounded by the documentation of the extreme injuries to his most recent victim and that fact that she was just one in a long list of women whose lives had been indelibly changed from the fears and injuries they experienced by his hand.

Mark had met his latest and newest victim in a bar. He recognized her extreme vulnerability to any kind of attention, let alone what he termed "honey talk," and invited her to come home with him.

After a couple days of drinking and rough sex, he bound her wrists with a lamp cord, beat her with his fists and a wooden hanger, burned her with a lightbulb and dragged her around the floor by a hairbrush twisted into her long hair. If he had not been so drunk, and she had not managed to get to the ringing phone just before he beat her for the last time, she would have died.

The person calling was the man's former girlfriend. The minute the receiver was lifted she immediately heard Backstrom's voice yelling something in the background about a "fucking bitch," after which the phone was dropped back on the cradle, ending the call.

The former girlfriend, sensing there was yet a new victim whose life was inches from coming to a brutal end, called the police claiming someone was in the process of robbing her and Mark's shared home and that law enforcement was needed immediately.

When the officers arrived at the front door, Mark denied that anyone else was in the residence. The officers apparently believed him and were about to leave. Then, as luck would have it, one noticed an open attic door in the upstairs hallway and said he needed to search the second floor.

The young woman was found unconscious and barely alive in the attic.

It took two months before she was physically able to speak about what happened. When she did talk, what she had to say was hampered by a mouthful of missing teeth and a fractured jaw. Like many women of this nature, her ongoing question was, "What did I do to make him so angry?"

In jail, Mark was the tough guy, boasting that his "old lady" made up false claims about him beating her when she was the one who had abused him. He cursed her and women in general, calling them overbearing and "just using men to get what they really wanted," as he laughed about what he was going to do when he "won one on her."

Despite his threats and bravado, his life was basically over. He had finally gotten himself into the system in a way that guaranteed a very long sentence. Instead of being the one giving orders, he was going to be following orders for a long time.

He would ultimately be sent to a Super Max prison where he reportedly cut out the liver of another inmate during a riot and threw the organ at the negotiators. He was the epitome of a stone-cold psychopath.

Chapter 11

Two days following Milton Beardsley's failure to show up at his annual May fishing outing, the police were at his house asking questions. Where exactly was he headed? Which road did he usually take to get there? What were the names of his fishing buddies? Were there any additional contacts or added information that could be helpful? Did he have a history of medical problems? Did he call to say he had arrived at his destination? What was the same or different from his normal routine?

The officers' next stop was Lake Crest Cemetery. The police searched his office, the entire crematorium, and the building where the shovels and lawn equipment were stored. One of the officers questioned what appeared to be blood on a shovel and tagged it to be sent to the crime lab for analysis. All of Milton's coworkers were interviewed. His office was searched.

The county law enforcement helicopter spent days searching the hillsides adjoining the highway Milton was assumed to have taken. The pilots found one area where it appeared that some kind of vehicle may have knocked down seedlings as it slid down the hillside, but no actual vehicle was found. They sent boats and divers to one portion of the river looking for a vehicle … a body … anything.

They finally did locate Milton's car, but it was in an unexpected area of the river. The problem was, there was no body, only fishing and camping equipment. The vehicle windows were all broken; the doors were damaged and hanging open. But Milton was nowhere to be found. The officers concluded that the preliminary information did not make sense; there were too many missing pieces, one being why the car was found in an unlikely location. More people needed to be interviewed.

Law enforcement issued missing person statements and bulletins in an attempt to add to and/or fill in the missing pieces of the puzzle, without success. Milton's fishing buddies were interviewed; his records had been accessed to see if and where he had used his credit cards for gas or food. Nothing turned up.

When the Lake Crest grounds crews were interviewed, no one reported any unusual activities. No one gave rise to suspicion with their manner of answering questions. No one was noted as having a criminal history or recent contact with law enforcement. No one at the cemetery knew Milton's fishing buddies. As was customary, the police ran records checks on all the cemetery employees, but no notable red flags turned up. Still, it seemed like something more was missing, besides Milton.

Since there was no body, Lake Crest held a memorial service. The hope remained that somewhere, somehow, sometime, his body would be recovered.

Also overlooked was the fact that the John Doe ashes were still waiting to be picked up—by someone. No one knew if anyone had called about them. No one knew anything.

Chapter 12

For Seth, however, there was very little time to grieve the loss of his colleague. His current challenge was that of preparing the body of twenty-eight-year-old Patricia Marston.

Patricia was the daughter of Blair Marston, a former state senator. She was a verbose and articulate television personality who interviewed local business leaders. She also filled in for news anchors and was respected for her knack for providing information to help voters choose the best candidates.

Stunning in appearance, and seen as a good and dependable friend, what added to her likability was her common sense and relaxed nature—and the fact that she did not appear to have a condescending bone in her body.

The carefully planned scuba diving vacation with a group of friends started out smoothly. Everyone met at the island beach hideaway, and they took turns cooking dinners or eating in the eclectic village eateries. At night, they talked around campfires, stargazed, and caught up in general. Each day began with early morning coffee to catch the sunrise followed by a planning session for the best dive area.

Patricia was part of this group that included old and new friends. Many of them were familiar with diving, some of them quite skilled. Others, like herself, were strong swimmers but had no formal scuba training.

On this particular day, the group was diving in fifty-to-seventy-five-foot depths, looking at underwater scenes of multicolored coral, vegetation, and endless varieties of fish and other sea life.

Patricia knew slightly more than the bottom-line basics of diving. For instance, she knew not to ascend faster than the bubbles from her exhaled air due to the possibility of an air embolism. Known as a calculated person and not one given to panic, she respected the combined wisdom of her fellow divers and did not hesitate to ask questions. As to the creatures that called this watery expanse their home, she saw herself as their casual visitor, if not a guest.

Throughout the morning, the group took breaks to exchange information, relocate to a new diving location, make additional plans, and deal with equipment issues. Those who were more familiar with the area shared details about the creatures, offered information related to plant life, and provided diving tips. Everyone had lunch on the boat and returned to the water in the afternoon.

Patricia always took a favorite underwater flash camera on these dives. While most underwater areas tended to appear rather bland to the natural eye, they exploded with color when captured by flash photography. She had entered previous photos in various competitions and had always enjoyed the comradery as well as the shared suggestions and lessons.

This afternoon's designated dive area included a large, rocky mass approximately twenty-five feet high and covered with moss and other plants. It caught her eye because of the myriad of sea life darting in and out of the many crevices. She was also fascinated with what seemed like an endless array of camera angles for capturing the best shots. She took one flash photo, then repositioned herself to capture the light coming over the top of the rocky mound.

She was especially attracted to one intricate, lacy fern that had made its home just under a large rocky ledge. After positioning herself and the camera to include the light coming over the mass, with the brightest light at the two o'clock position, she snapped the photo.

Acquiring more confidence, she crept closer to the fern and its rocky home, preparing to take a second photo. Suddenly, out of nowhere lunged two giant Moray eels.

The heads of the Morays were the size of large dogs. Their jaws were wide open, displaying threatening, cavernous mouths lined with rows of pointed, glass-sharp teeth. Their serpentine bodies were not only ugly, but also evil in appearance and size—especially their piercing, dead-looking, blank eyes.

Patricia froze. The Morays stormed her like ugly sea creatures from hell protecting their home. One of the eels got tangled in her camera strap, breaking it while it was still connected to her left wrist and jarring her into the reality of her tenuous situation. Patricia quickly realized she was more than an uninvited intruder—she was a target.

Her earlier confidence was shattered and reduced her to the reality that, in this underwater setting, she was the clear neophyte. For the first time ever, Patricia experienced an unknown and immense fear, greater than anything she had felt before.

Her raw impression was that the eels' primary intent was attacking and killing anything competing for space or food. What began as a pleasant dive had now been transformed into an underwater nightmare. She saw herself as the prey! She was in a state of emotional free-fall.

Patricia's sole impulse was to get to a point of survival as fast as possible. Putting one foot on the rocky wall, she pushed away with all her might. She scrambled to find the toggle on her buoyancy compensator, knowing this action could rocket her to the safety of the surface.

Unfortunately, she failed to exhale while she shot upward toward assumed safety. She escaped the eels but died in the process.

The boat captain saw the body break the surface and yelled, "We got a problem here! Get in the water and move that diver to the swim deck!" Before he even finished his sentence, two crewmembers were in the water making their way to Patricia. Obviously lifeless.

"My god, what happened?" yelled one of her rescuers. "She's gone!"

They pulled Patricia onto the swim deck and removed her mask. It was filled with blood and froth. "What a hell of a way to die. Her lungs burst; there is nothing we can do."

They stood in silence over the body out of respect and, at the same time, terrified at what had happened.

Minutes later, other divers reached the surface one by one and instantly recognized the tragedy before their eyes. They knew from the expressions on the crewmembers' faces that the worst had happened. They looked at their friend's lifeless body and her bloody face. Eventually someone broke the silence. "We have to call her father and find out what to do."

They hugged each other, some crying, and tried to understand how this could have happened. How can you be having a fantastic time one minute, and seconds later, someone is dead?

It was too much. Too soon. Too awful to believe. Some argued that they should have grabbed her and held her from rushing to the surface. Others stated that such heroics would have caused more harm. On the way to shore, they discussed who would call her father. It was going to be a long night.

Normally, when a person dies outside of the US, local authorities perform a cursory evaluation, and bodies are embalmed in the country where the death occurred. Some countries require autopsies prior to shipment of the remains, even in cases of accidental death. The costs vary and tend to be expensive.

Because Patricia's father had connections for just such a situation, an emergency air ambulance was dispatched. The paperwork was expedited, allowing Patricia's body to be transported back to the States immediately.

The news of the drowning left everyone shocked. Her parents, siblings, and extended family struggled to think of her being forever gone without their having a chance to say goodbye. It only got worse as her funeral date approached.

Her family brought Seth one of Patricia's most beautiful purple strapless evening gowns. He rose to the occasion, swallowing hard to be working on someone who had been a friend. As usual, he first set her jaw, then the eyes, then concocted the perfect mixture of embalming ingredients. He fused all incision sites with super glue to make them smooth and air brushed her body until she looked like a perfectly tanned sleeping beauty, dreaming of white sandy beaches and listening to the laughter of nearby friends.

He had the hairdresser wash, dry, and style her long, thick, shiny black hair. He dressed her in the evening gown and carefully arranged her hair around her face. He placed a tiny bouquet of pink, purple, and white flowers in her hands, a final touch that even made his assistant tear up and turn away. Patricia looked regal and as astonishingly gorgeous in death as she had been in life.

Her parents brought Patricia's black lab, Milly, to the funeral home. The dog became excited when she heard her mistress's name, as though she was going to get to be with her. She paced back and forth at the house and became even more excited and eager in the car—moving from one side to the other, as though this would make the trip shorter.

When the family arrived, Milly seemed thrilled to be part of the event. Then upon entering the funeral home and sensing death, she became still, anxious, and then somber. As they entered the room where Patricia's coffin was located, Milly froze in place.

Milly could see Patricia laying in the coffin. Obviously, something terrible had happened. She started to whine and stayed crouched beside Patricia's father's feet. Eventually she put her front paws on the side of the casket and sniffed her mistress, casting furtive glances at the family to do something … anything … to make Patricia be herself again.

Finally accepting death and the fact that nothing could be done, Milly lay beside the casket, getting up every so often to approach Patricia's friends and to check to see if anything had changed. She repeated this cycle again and again.

Friends and family shared attempts at reassuring the dog, and both groups were comforted by Milly's display of loyalty and love of her mistress. Although gut wrenchingly sad, no one would have not wanted Milly there. This was a difficult reviewal for a lot of people, even the people at the funeral home.

The eventual presence of political figures, media folks, neighbors, former classmates, and others became a welcome distraction. Milly wandered from group to group, as though that was what she needed to do. The funeral, as usual, became a sorrowful social event as well as a celebration of a beautiful, albeit short, life. Most guests followed along to Patricia's burial site for the brief service at her final resting place.

Chapter 13

Lake Crest Cemetery had never had a need for night guards because the funeral directors were on the premises 24/7, and staff and deliveries were typically coming and going without pause. Yet, unbeknownst to anyone, an unknown soul had been added to Patricia's open grave and covered with some of the nearby fresh soil during the darkness of night.

After each grave was dug, extra earth was piled nearby, then covered with a grass-like carpet, if such a space next to the burial spot existed. If there was no room for the dirt at the burial site, it was hauled away and returned when the coffin had been placed in the vault and the grave was ready to be re-filled.

The burial vault crew arrived early every morning while it was still dark, usually on the day of the scheduled service. They lowered the vault into the grave, reserving the immense cover and storing it close by. Then a tent was set up to prevent the vault from filling with possible rain.

After the funeral ceremony and departure of guests, the last of the extra soil was added to the grave, and in a matter of minutes, it would look like the grave had been there forever. Unlike the family grief, which was only beginning.

Daily life at the cemetery continued. Florists' vans came and went, chairs were set up and wiped off. Tracks from the vault truck, if there were any, were hosed clean. Nothing appeared out of order. Nothing.

Chapter 14

Susan was pulling into a nearby Texaco station to get gas for her drive north for an interview with a state prison inmate. While waiting for her tank to fill, she noticed a local newspaper headline: the police had arrested a man as a suspect in the killing of a young runaway.

The girl was sixteen, Caucasian, and had yet to be claimed by her family. She ran away at fourteen, reportedly living on the streets as a prostitute. Her body was ultimately found when the stench of her death caused neighbors to complain to the landlord. Authorities quickly determined that she had been sexually assaulted and had been dead for several days.

Here was a young girl whose life had been more than a mere challenge for a long, long time. Susan thought back to her own youth, sheltered for sure by some standards, but also rich with opportunities for deep friendships, favorite teachers, education, and music lessons. After a few blissful moments thinking about her copacetic, long-ago prairie home, her mind started to drift to what Frank Phillips, the alleged perpetrator she was about to interview, would say about his life.

In the margins of the records, she had added notes to the effect of "Ask about this … what does this mean to him? What happened as a result of this situation?"

It was oftentimes fascinating to learn who or what had influenced the lives of the people she interviewed, choices they made, regrets, if any, and the best and worst times. She wanted to confirm or challenge her interpretation of the person's situation. When she was incorrect or miles from the truth, she gained surprisingly helpful information to clarify data and make her reports more accurate and helpful.

Susan parked her car in the prison parking lot, gathered her briefcase and coat, and walked to the entrance. She greeted the prison staff and asked if they knew when Frank's attorney would be arriving. She waited while the contents of her briefcase were searched. As she repacked her briefcase, she added the extra manilla tablet she had carried by hand from her car. She hung up her coat and walked through the metal detector, clearing it.

She remembered a one-time experience when she was wearing an underwire bra, which set off the detector. She actually had to go to the ladies' room to remove the bra, place it in a paper bag, and walk through the screening area for a second time. She never made that mistake again.

Since the client's attorney had not yet arrived, Susan found an empty chair near a sunny window and sat down to wait. It was toasty warm in the prison waiting area, and the aroma of fresh coffee permeated the air. Prison staff had stamped the back of her hand with a mark that only showed under ultraviolet light, verifying her status of being permitted to both enter and exit the prison.

When Frank Phillips's attorney arrived, brief pleasantries were exchanged. The attorney indicated he did not need to talk with his client, prompting the interview to start a few minutes early. Susan preferred the chair directly across from the interviewee, and Frank's attorney sat at the end of the table, near his client.

"Good morning, Mr. Phillips. My name is Dr. Kasson. I am a psychologist asked by the court to review your records and meet with you about your case." She informed Frank about the purpose of the interview and indicated that if at any time he needed or wanted to talk privately with his attorney, he should let her know, and she would step out of the room.

She explained that the interview would be recorded and asked Frank to let her know if he did not understand any of the words she used or the questions she asked. She asked him if he was ready to begin, and he nodded in agreement.

Frank was a twenty-three-year-old white male who had a criminal history beginning at the age of fourteen, including attacking an adult female whose car he had stolen. At knifepoint, he forced this woman to drive to a remote area, disrobe, and perform oral sex on him—or be killed. This nightmare lasted nearly two hours before he disappeared into the darkness of night, leaving the woman abandoned in the woods. When she realized he was gone for good, she found her way to a highway and waved to drivers until someone stopped to give her a ride to a hospital.

Frank's life history, at least since the age of six, included a revolving door of out-of-home placements due to his pattern of alleged disruptive and aggressive behaviors. His mother was a drug addict when she was pregnant with Frank, suggesting he too may have suffered from her substance abuse.

As a child, he assaulted other children without provocation, attacked female teachers, and approached adult female strangers oddly, touching their clothing and exhibiting behavior strongly suggesting that he had observed adult sexual acts. He also had volatile temper issues. He could curse like an adult, fight like an animal, and was assessed and given trials of all sorts of medication in an attempt to curb his anger and behavior—without a drop of success.

He received sex offender treatment in his youth following sexual assault in a foster home and spent three years in a county correctional facility for teens.

Immediately upon release, he attacked an adult female stranger, thereby extending his probation. While visiting family in a nearby city, he was arrested for attempted robbery of a woman he followed to work. She claimed she thought he was going to rape her, had she not called out for help from strangers passing by.

Frank was an athletic looking male who, even in jail found a fellow inmate to neatly craft his head of cornrows. Frank could be polite, if not charming, and maintained a smooth and manipulative presentation throughout the four-hour interview.

Frank said his two convictions were "misunderstandings," explaining that in the first incident, his intention was "just to rob the lady" and adding he had "no idea" why it had gotten sexual. He scoffed at the idea of his allegedly forcing her to perform oral sex on him.

Despite police records noting descriptions of his behavior as reported by the victim, he denied threatening to kill her if she did not cooperate or that he showed her his gun, as well as denying he forcefully removed her clothing. He persisted in labeling her account as "full of lies and exaggerated," adding he pled guilty only because his attorney told him to do so. He said no one told him his rights, and that at the time, he did not understand his rights.

He also described the formal account of his second offense as "full of lies" and said he was only flirting, and "that wasn't a crime." He reported that he locked the door of his victim's apartment because she asked him to do so and that he "did not notice her acting afraid and certainly did not know her arm was pinned behind her back when he pressed her to the wall."

He reported leaving the scene because he "had another girlfriend waiting" and said he was "shocked that the woman said she was so afraid of him that she packed her things and moved out of state."

He described his best characteristics as "my ability to help my friends, be friendly, know how to have fun, and how to treat a lady," adding, "Women see me as charming because I like to talk; they say I'm sexy." He would further add he had a talent for writing screenplays, and when released, was going to go to acting school. He talked about how he had become a Christian in prison and brought his Bible with him to the evaluation.

When asked what tools he had to prevent his behavior repeating, he paused as though stunned, or confused, by the question. He then mentally regrouped and spoke about having a loving stepfather waiting to help him in any way possible, adding they would work together building cabinets in the family carpentry shop. Little did he know that Susan had already contacted this stepfather who said he "barely knew Frank, and what he did know of him was that he was a huge liar."

A month later during his court trial, Frank repeated his exaggerated description of his virtues. Unfortunately for him, each of his three female victims also presented their versions of his behaviors against them, initially in shaky voices that advanced to tearful recollections in which they reported that they thought they were going to be killed.

Whether by nature or nurture or both, Frank Phillips was a man without a conscience. His risk for reoffending remained high and unchanged, with research noting psychopaths have a five-times greater risk of reoffending when released from confinement.

After the trial, while stopping for gas for the trip home, Susan stood watching fellow travelers coming and going at the Travel Stop. The rhythmic bell on the pump counted off and paralleled her successive thoughts. *Normal appearing folks* she thought, *like Frank Phillips, who for all practical purposes look harmless.* It had always surprised her that so many high-risk offenders looked basically average. She hoped the young victims would be able, with time, to go on with the activities of ordinary living like the people at the Travel Stop.

That weekend, Susan's plans included attending a community fundraising dinner with a few friends she had not seen for way too long. One of the people who would be there was Detective Ken Russell and his wife Nita. Ken was a former Army Ranger who in his midlife had become a sheriff's deputy, ultimately deemed Law Enforcement Officer of the Year by the state's highest law enforcement agency.

Susan originally met Ken years prior when they were both involved in the same case. Ken, then a deputy, was assisting the sheriff in inviting an expert from the FBI academy in Quantico to come to their county to testify as an expert for the case.

The lawyer for the defendant called Susan to see if she would come to the courthouse to listen to this expert and assist in qualifying him. Susan agreed and asked the attorney to bring the expert's professional vita with him to court.

The claimed expert's vita noted no background, training, or education in clinical psychology, no degree in any field warranting his qualifying as being knowledgeable in mental health issues or any of the behavioral sciences. He had never been employed in a mental health treatment setting, nor did his vita speak to his having any training in diagnosing mental disorders, let alone treating them.

On the stand, the agent described his job as "reviewing the literature on a particular crime and comparing the information with the person's behavior, testifying in court as to his findings and opinion related to such."

Making matters worse for this FBI man was the fact that the *Frye criteria* used at the time for qualifying an expert required "clear demonstration that the individual being vetted demonstrated more training, skills, and experience than that of a common layman."

The absence of specific knowledge or training, like no clinical degree supporting his skill set along with his self-reported and limited training, basically prompted the judge to quickly disqualify him as an expert.

Then-deputy Russell inquired who Susan was; the defense lawyer then introduced her as new to the community and asked about her education, training, internships, board certifications, and various work settings. The judge nodded, and the rest of the case proceeded.

What made this situation especially sweet was the FBI agent's dramatic entrance to the humble county courthouse in his navy-blue, double-breasted jacket with his dashing and confident, if not flourishing, style. He swaggered into the courtroom as though he was easily smarter and more important than any country bumpkin there and what was going to happen would be, for him, a piece of cake.

Instead, he was methodically and completely discredited as an expert for the court, before the eyes of the humble county employees, the attorneys who were present, Dr. Kasson (the actual expert), and other courtroom staff. Surely this had been a painful object lesson in humility and the perils of inflating your status and training.

Chapter 15

The gala was elegant and relaxing, and the food bountiful and perfectly prepared. There was more seafood than even Neptune could have imagined or eaten: chilled shrimp on mountains of ice extending the length of the table, crab legs, and oysters. There were lavish salads, a variety of potato dishes, golden mounds of fried chicken, and several huge standing rib roasts, pink-rare in the center, along with a plethora of amazingly beautiful desserts. This was a feast for kings, topped off by the steady flow of champagne, wines, and whatever your thirst could imagine. Added to the menu were many heartfelt conversations of friends who needed to see each other more often.

After dinner, Ken and Susan caught up on a nearby patio over glasses of Maker's Mark. "What's up with the newspaper accounts of several missing people?" asked Susan.

"Yeah," responded Ken, "the numbers keep growing, and the clues remain perplexing. The cases are dissimilar and from all parts of the city. Just average folks living average lives who all of a sudden are reported missing without a trace. Very perplexing."

Susan sipped on her Maker's before asking, "What about the missing woman who was just in the paper. Did anything turn up on her?"

"Anne Tolbar, the nurse? Basically nothing. It's like she just disappeared into thin air. Usually we get some calls, especially if a photo is attached to a story." Smiling, he added, "Not even our psychic sources have come up with anything. The only case we have partial closure, until we can look into it more closely, is the cemetery supervisor. We found his car and some personal items in the river. The strange thing is, there were no bones in the vehicle or nearby. Organic material does not last forever, but it can take a while for bones to completely disappear. While searching for Beardsley, we found some skeletal remains of missing persons that had been submerged for a period of time, based on the decomposition of the body and dates on the car plates. But, no trace of him. Very puzzling."

Ken stopped talking to take a sip of his drink, looking contemplative. He continued, "We talked to his coworkers, and they said he was going to drive up north for a fishing trip with friends. Problem is, the road he took to supposedly get there was not in the right direction. We are still working on the case."

Then turning to Susan, Ken asked, "What's new in your part of the world? Figured out how to cure lying and bullshit yet?"

Susan smiled and replied, "Now what would keep us fascinated if it weren't for BS and lying? That's what keeps us searching for the truth, right? Interviews would be so easy if only the truth was told—and if it matched with other facts, that is. Actually, Ken, my interest and concern has been piqued by the mention of these missing people. Where are they? I am seeing articles where family members are asking the public for any information anyone has to share. Imagine someone you care about just disappearing completely. Especially if it was someone who worked beside you. If I were going to take off for a while, someone would know where I was or could be—but these people are just ... gone!"

While Susan took a sip of her bourbon, Ken got out his phone and opened up a folder related to a recent "S & T meeting."

"This represents Stats and Technical data research we are organizing. It is a new department set up a year ago to gather, study, and analyze crime stats, trends, cases, and so forth. The new programmer is amazing. He has entered all the crimes committed in the city in the past five years and broken them into categories, with repeat offenders highlighted. He also noted which parole officers have the best records of working with certain types of offenders, which programs show signs of really being helpful, and the offenders with the worst recidivism records.

"He has broken down the city into sectors where certain crimes are most rampant, marking what crimes occur there, what programs are in existence, and the names of contact personnel. We now know, for instance, that heroin is the big drug on the western edge of town, more than any other substance, and we know where most of it is coming from. We also know that drug programs in the schools may be helpful for kids to connect with law enforcement staff but do little to curb drug use. You should come to one of these meetings; they are fascinating."

"It sounds great, Ken. Let me know the next time there is a meeting, and I'll be there. What do the stats say about sex offenses and offenders in the area?"

"This city and sector map identifies where every registered offender lives . . ."

"God, the area is speckled with them!" Susan exclaimed.

Ken continued, "I found out there is one guy who lives five blocks from my house in a ritzy area. We have everyone's name who is registered, circled with another color if they have a history of failing to register, and best of all, we have color coding for other offenders who have an adult history of sex offense but were never required to register because of the laws at the times of their offenses. Only flaw is that offenders charged as juveniles are not on the map. You can't get into their files other than to scan their adult record to note references to similar activity in their youth."

"What do the stats say about murder?"

"Well, the city has a rather low murder rate that seems to be steady over time, at least for the past ten years, typically in the low 30s for a year. That is up from ten years ago like you cannot believe, but the problem is that murders, suicides, and accidental deaths are skewed by who did what to each entry. Some so-called suicides could have been carefully staged murders. Suicides have been steady over time, typically greater activity among single or divorced males ages twenty-eight to fifty. One surprising trend is the number of kids who are killing themselves. Some kids have suicided because they realize they are gay, and their parents made it clear that was unacceptable."

"Tragic. That's something I'll never understand. Any info on rapes?"

"Well, we're working on that. That's another reason you should call and get on the resource list. Rapes, as you know, can be underreported or falsely reported. The stats say 245 were reported over the past five years, but only 120 resulted in convictions. Does that mean the others were false reports or changed thanks to some silver-tongued liars, oh, sorry, lawyers? The trend seems to pair rapes rising in relation to substance abuse and, of all things, the seasons ... can you believe that? When it's hot, some guys get trashed and force women to have sex."

"I believe it, alright. I've seen it time and again. Any unexpected findings?"

"There are always unexpected findings," replied Ken with a chuckle. "That's why the data, and specifically the group, is so vital. It keeps us open to the unexpected, atypical situation and the paranormal. It makes us flexible."

"I'll bet." Susan smiled.

"One of the craziest stats is the number of missing persons' reports by family members for all age ranges, but predominately adult females. Some of these women seem to just disappear, never return, and are never found. We are expanding our current interstate network to see if we can make some connections. It's a big job, as you might imagine."

"I'm sure some women just move and don't tell their families." Susan could think of a few women who had left in the night to escape abusive situations.

"Of course, people move for whatever reason. But, others seem to have careers and friends, and then all of a sudden, they are gone without a trace. The leads go dead, and the years pass by."

Ken stood up to get a drink of water, still talking, "Take for instance the Nickerson case ten years ago. Beautiful woman, smart, articulate, and successful by all reports—even lived in a gated community. She was in line for a higher position in the Vela Financial Group, and one day she failed to show up for work. We had staff on that case for six years without a single credible clue. To this day, she is still missing and presumed dead. Believe me, we had psychics calling, crazy calls from people who wanted information, crank calls, you name it. We checked out every possible clue and got zip."

Susan responded, "That is shocking!"

"Then there was the Mariotti case. She was the lead ballerina for the Hallen Dance Group and disappeared while reportedly on her way to her mother's funeral out east. Nothing was disturbed in her apartment; people had talked to her and knew of her travel plans, but she just never returned. There was not a single clue; no one knew or saw anything. She just seemed to vanish. That case was seven years ago, and every one of her family members has called over time, still struggling with the fact that we are unable to find her."

"I don't blame the family. It's the not knowing that's so troubling."

"So true. In the past five years, there have been forty of these cases. Five have been found, and the rest—just question marks for which we have no answers. It hurts to say we were no help at all; what happened to these folks?

"Just like that nurse, Anne Tolbar. She worked at St. Boniface's and disappeared after her night shift. Her father is Ben Tobar, our dispatcher. We talked to both Ben and his wife, the woman's last boyfriend, her neighbors, her friends, and her landlord. Nothing. No one saw or knew anything. No one heard anything. She had plans to have her usual weekly lunch with her mother on Wednesday and never showed up. Her car was in her garage, and nothing was amiss in her apartment. Maybe she will show up next month and say she decided to be a Las Vegas dancer. But I doubt it. It's not looking good at this point."

Susan looked at her watch and sighed, "I wish we could talk more, but I need to get home. I have an early evaluation in the morning at Carrington State Hospital. The S &T group sounds fascinating. Send me the date of the next meeting."

Ken took a last sip of his Maker's and said he would do just that. He also added his usual parting comment, "Keep your powder dry."

"I will," replied Susan. "You too!"

Chapter 16

Seth Loring arrived at the funeral home early on Monday. With him as usual, was his brother, Sam. Sam went directly to the garage to have a cup of coffee with the other workers and prepare for his day of varied tasks. Seth walked into the funeral home, noticing a pink phone message taped to his door. At the same time, his cell phone rang.

"Hey, Mr. Loring, this is Phil at the crematorium, and I have a question. We have a box of ashes from the retort that we have been holding for two months, waiting for someone to claim them. There was a problem with the original paperwork, and no contact person was identified. Also, some of the documents are missing or have omissions or errors, such as no authorization or permit for cremation, no death certificate, and no verification that the cost of cremation would be covered by the county. We did wait the customary twenty-four hours after receiving the body before we proceeded to the cremation, but now, we don't know what to do. These ashes have been here since May 12."

Seth, paused to consider the situation, distracted momentarily by the stated date of May 12, as that particular date was near the death and loss of one of his best workers, namely, Milton Beardsley.

"Everything will work out fine, Phil. We can just hold on to the ashes. Attach a note to the box of cremains referencing this conversation and be sure to sign and date it. It sounds like somebody new was involved along the chain of events, but everything will be okay." Phil sounded relieved, thanked Seth for his help, and ended the call.

As Phil attached his note to the box of ashes and placed them on the shelf he was thinking, *Who would forget to pick up someone's ashes? What would it be like to die and be forgotten completely? What is this person's family going to feel like when they do call and realize how long it took to pick up these remains?* When he saw the number of boxes left on the shelf marked HOLDING/TO BE PICKED UP, he was even more chagrined. "What is this world coming to?" he muttered.

Chapter 17

In her batch of mail, Susan received a letter from the local law enforcement committee requesting her presence as part of a team looking into the crime issues in Rockford City. She determined that this was compliments of Detective Ken Russell. The first meeting of the group was scheduled in two weeks.

As she made the two-hour drive to the Juvenile Detention Center, Susan started thinking seriously about joining the group. She was excited about learning from such a team, and since she worked cases from all over the state, she considered the possibility that she might be in a position to identify trends, as well as learn about and identify new resources.

Arriving at Many Rivers Detention Center, Susan gathered her paperwork and braced for the thirty-minute process of showing her identification papers and passing a highly sensitive metal detector easily triggered by eyeglasses, jewelry, zippers. and whatever else. She talked to multiple unseen people whose voices guided her along the way and verified who she was and the reason for her visit.

The clear voices would open metal doors at certain points, allowing her to enter. The electronic doors would slowly close behind her with the customary dead bolt firing into place. Then she would proceed to the interview area and sit waiting for staff to bring the adolescent to her.

Some of the kids had histories that spoke to their slim chances in life based on their gene pool and home environment. Others lived in settings of domestic violence, poverty, rampant substance abuse, inconsistent parenting (not that any parents are perfectly consistent all of the time), multiple caregivers as marriages failed, a revolving door of new "stepparents," and a myriad of different surnames, as though that was the norm.

Other kids had seemingly raised themselves, angry and defiant of rules and expectations that, to them, made no sense. Susan often wondered how the bad habits seemed to be passed, seemingly by osmosis, to yet uncorrupted good kids so easily.

She remembered one sad story she had been told by a youngster when she first started her job—that of an eleven-year-old boy who reported going into gas station restrooms on a daily basis after school to pilfer rolls of toilet paper for his brothers, sisters, and his mother at home.

Mostly, she remembered how casually he talked about the routineness of this part of his day. It was a conflicting combination of his historically documented criminal behavior with glimpses of his personal acts of thoughtfulness. This was a childhood she had no familiarity with except for that of the youth and adults she interviewed.

Her current evaluation was related to twelve-year-old Benjamin Nichols, a white male admitted to the center three months prior due to self-injurious behavior at home and property destruction in the form of putting holes in walls and breaking doors, toys, and chairs. He had most recently been charged with Fifth Degree Assault for attacking treatment center staff.

His working diagnoses was Mood Disorder, Not Otherwise Specified, with anxious and depressive symptoms, past history of obsessive-compulsive disorder, oppositional defiant disorder, ADHD, and a rule out for atypical autism. He was prescribed Depakote and Paxil, a mood stabilizer, and an antidepressant. Since being admitted to the center, his parents had filed for divorce.

The court order was to determine whether Ben, as he liked to be called, was competent to stand trial, able to understand the legal proceedings pending against him, and demonstrate the ability to participate in his own defense. In English this meant, did he understand what was involved in his going to court, and more importantly, could he distinguish when and how to be self-protective with regards to his legal situation?

Before she met with this youngster, Susan reviewed the incident report, the boy's treatment records including the facility's account of the incident, his diagnosis, medication list, and noted behavioral problems as well as collateral references. When she had enough additional background information, she informed the staff she was ready to talk to him in person.

Ben was casually dressed and adequately groomed. He sported a four-inch afro and a skinny and fragile stature. His long history of problems included a revolving door of unstable caregivers, repeated moves, and frequently changing schools. He was polite to Susan. She introduced herself and encouraged him to ask questions if and when he did not understand what she was saying.

Ben indicated he had been to court before on one previous occasion, which to Susan was a hopeful sign that he was on some level aware of the seriousness of his situation. He was able to accurately define the word "assault," stating, "You hit someone when they least expect it."

When asked if this was a serious charge, Ben answered again in the affirmative, and when asked the reason, he reported, "Someone could get hurt." However, when asked the penalty if the person was found guilty of such a charge, he responded, "I don't know."

He was unable to identify his attorney by name and stated he was "not sure" what his attorney's job was in the case. When asked if his attorney was a defense or prosecuting attorney, he asked for the meaning of the word, "prosecuting" and then said he still did not know the answer to the question.

He was able to state his attorney would be "for me" and that his attorney's job was to "help me." He was unable to explain the county attorney's role, and when asked if this attorney was "also for him" he responded, "I'm not sure."

When asked the judge's role in the courtroom, Ben reported, "He listens ... he will find out what will happen to me." When asked how the judge arrived at his decision, Ben stated, "I don't know." He defined a "witness" as "someone who saw what happened." When asked to define the words, "jury" and "oath," he reported not knowing what either word meant.

When asked how a person should behave in court, Ben responded, "Respect the judge," defining "respect" as "be nice; don't be violent." When asked when he should speak in court, he responded, "When the judge says so."

When asked what he could do if he heard lies about him in court, he said, "Stand up and say, 'Your Honor, that's not true.'" When asked who he could talk with if he had any questions about what was occurring in court, such as words that were being used or what was happening, he stated, "Your attorney." When asked his attorney's name, he stated he had "forgotten it."

When asked what could happen if a person were found guilty, Ben stated, "He could be sent to a bad place." When asked what could happen if a person was found not guilty, he stated, "I don't know." When given a choice of going home or somewhere else that was confining, he responded, "Home." He denied knowing the meaning of the word "plea bargaining."

When Ben was asked his version of the events that took place on the day of the alleged assault, his account was strikingly different from the official incident report by the police and made Susan wonder whether staff at the center had attempted to assist him in finding words to describe his actions. Additional records noted Ben having a pattern of telling different people different stories or accounts of what happened and giving his parents inaccurate information about what had occurred at the treatment center.

His records noted a Full Scale IQ of 86, meaning a low average level of intelligence. He was not seen as exhibiting a specific learning disability but rather demonstrating a history of expressive language disabilities, including a slight speech problem. His receptive language skills were identified as falling in the High Average range, suggesting he understood language at a higher level than what he was able to communicate.

Personality-wise, he was seen as endorsing symptoms of dysphoria; his biggest struggles were identified as coping with peers, fear of rejection and abandonment, and his open concern about his parents' pending divorce.

Other records noted staff had commented on Ben's quickly changing moods. Also noted was the Fifth Degree Assault charge resulting after Ben kicked one staff member in the face when he was about to be freed from restraint.

Susan thanked Ben for his time talking with her and wished him well. She gathered her paperwork and went through the exiting process to get out of the building. Her car was warm from sitting in the sun for a couple hours, so she stood outside and made a couple phone calls. Then she headed home.

Her report would say that Ben did not demonstrate being competent to stand trial. Specifically, he demonstrated little knowledge of the adversarial nature of the court system and lacked insight into his own behavior. He remained impulsive and did not demonstrate the ability to assist his attorney.

As often happens during the drive, Susan's mind entertained thoughts as to how kids like Ben happen, where he might end up, and the obstacles in his path.

Her thoughts were completely random combinations of issues including the juvenile center itself, the contrast of her childhood versus that of the boy Ben she had just interviewed, her upcoming schedule, and oddly enough, the expanding case related to Milton Beardsley. Something seemed amiss, but she couldn't put her finger on it.

Chapter 18

Back in her office, Susan was working on the case of Thomas Clemson, an allegedly repeat sex offender.

Hired guns could be found for either side, the defense or prosecution. Not easily recognizable at first. Sometimes you can tell who they are by what they say, how they say it, and by their track records. If an expert testifies in numerous cases, and 98 percent of the time comes to the same opinion, they could be a garden variety hired gun serving the interests of whoever is paying them. This can be an extremely profitable if not a lucrative business.

Susan remembered one call she received by an attorney who asked her to see his client, adding, "We don't want him to be found incompetent to stand trial, but we need him to get off the streets." After listening more to the script she was being given, she begged off the case, stating her calendar was full this time but to please call again if she could be of help.

Simple also, was the fact that people who hire these folks always know they will get what they pay for and expect. This situation has and always will exist in adversarial settings. On one occasion, an attorney-colleague told Susan that the same was true in medical malpractice cases. He said 85 percent or greater of such cases were reportedly won by the defense (the doctor) because when it looked like there might be a chance of the plaintiff winning, other doctors would be called as experts, reporting they would have performed the same examinations, found similar results, and therefore no standard of care had been breached.

In Susan's review of the current case, the man's history and several hours of interview/testing combined had formed her opinion, as the first examiner, that this man had an antisocial personality disorder and alcohol dependency. His criminal history did include two alleged sexual assaults, one as a juvenile—in the midst of numerous fights, burglaries, property damage, and alcohol-related offenses—and another as an adult. But, in Susan's review of the case, he did not meet the criteria for that of a sexual predator. This case was going to be one of those times when her opinion could contribute to blocking the wrong outcome and preventing an injustice. Maybe.

Thomas Clemson was now in his late twenties. He had violated the conditions of his probation on various occasions by becoming intoxicated and missing work and appointments with his probation officer, who eventually pulled the plug on his stayed sentence, resulting in his return to prison. Big price to pay for a few beers. When Clemson's release was imminent, due to what appeared to be his predatory history, he became the subject of an exit interview, and a petition to commit him as a sexually dangerous person commenced. This type of commitment is indeterminant, meaning it could last his lifetime.

His sexual offenses included the lower-level criminal sexual conduct conviction at the age of twelve, when he and four other male friends grabbed a female classmate and wrestled her to the ground.

They attempted unsuccessfully to remove her clothing, so instead touched her sexually over her clothing. This happened in broad daylight. All the kids knew each other, and a passerby ran to her aid, ending the incident. The police were called.

The girl was unsure who of the boys was actually involved in directly touching her because she was scrambling to get free. She thought two of the boys, neither of which was Thomas, had been more involved than Thomas. Transcripts of police interviews with the teenagers also indicated two boys, neither of them Thomas, had been identified as the instigators and leaders in the incident.

The two boys implicated, however, were accompanied by their parents to the police station and pointed the finger at Thomas, the well-known troublemaker from a dysfunctional minority family. In exchange for their agreeing to testify against him, their charges were dropped, and a less than clear event became a small version of a witch hunt. Ultimately, Thomas was the only one of the four boys who was charged with and convicted of the offense. With plea bargaining he was placed on probation.

Because of his prior sexual assault, his attorney told Thomas he did not have a good chance of beating the charge, and it would be best to plead guilty and take the best deal he could get. Because of the state laws where he lived, the deal would include his having to register as a sex offender for the next ten years. He subsequently married, had a family, worked sporadically, and continued to be arrested on occasion for drinking and fighting, eventually going to prison to serve his sentence for violating the conditions of his probation.

When Susan reviewed the transcripts of his previous court proceedings, she took careful notes of questions she wanted to ask to clarify each of the two offenses. During the interview with him, he openly reported ongoing resentment for what had happened to him. He owned his alcohol dependency and remarked about his new abstinent life accomplished through incarceration.

His scores on actuarial risk assessment instruments were in the Low to Moderate range related to static (unchangeable) factors such as his current age, past convictions, not having victims who were strangers to him or males, and having a history of non-sexual assaults. On an actuarial risk instrument, changeable risk factors such as his now being a recovering alcoholic, returning to a supportive family system, and other testing indicating NO evidence of his having been designated a psychopath, his overall score spoke to a lower risk for re-offense and reconviction.

While incarcerated, he had completed classes in anger management, critical thinking, parenting, and men's issues. He had also attended AA meetings and participated in a sex offender group. A personality inventory completed by Thomas was that common to an individual with an antisocial personality disorder history. Collateral sources of information, like people who had worked with him and those he would report to, spoke of Thomas having improved his behavior and his attitude.

At some point as a psychological examiner, you have to arrive at an opinion, preferably one consistent with the evidence. Your opinion then puts you on one side of the adversarial fence or the other, the defense or the prosecution.

It can be a lonely spot because for some attorneys, you are only a temporary commodity, helpful for their cause, not yours. They, however, cannot always do it alone. If you help them win their case, they look good because they included you in the equation.

So, a short time later, Susan found herself in court, sitting for four days while a suave expert orator mesmerized the judge with his reported extensive research knowledge and opinions—absent his having interviewed Thomas in person. To Susan, this was more than disturbing. Although she had long ago learned not to become invested in the outcome of a case, it was impossible not to react internally on some level.

She hoped she at least looked calm on her exterior. As an expert, she was expected to comment on the ultimate issue, but it was the court who would make the final decision.

Listening to this man twist Thomas's history and exaggerate the psychological testing scores as indicative of truly psychopathic personality—despite evidence within the record to the contrary—was endlessly painful. What made it worse was the fact that Susan's report was misstated by the other psychologist and included his incorporating some of her supposedly erroneous testing results into his display of assumed prowess.

She had watched him talk with the state's attorney before court and suspected they were colluding on the best strategy to win the case. That was the goal in some cases—winning.

Because her opinion put her on the side of the defense, Susan would be the last to testify. She would follow the testimony of the other professionals whose record reviews of the case excluded direct contact with Thomas, and she would follow another second examiner who was known for changing his mind—and doing so at the last minute so as to cast doubt by acting as though he just now came to a new conclusion that the respondent did meet the criteria for being dangerous and needed to be confined to protect the community.

The opinion could take ninety days. The judge came across as a reasonable man. This same judge was also the judge for Thomas's case in his youth, and she had carefully couched her statements regarding the juvenile offense as referring to the records, including transcripts of the case in which the victim clearly stated Thomas was not the perpetrator, even though his friends had sold him out.

An evening of fireworks was a great distraction for Susan's tension. While still feeling the toll of the case in her heart and bones, she began to relax and enjoy the visual festivities. She was aware she was numb to the sound of the nearby laughing children and the view of happy families gathered together.

The evening was a delightful array of music, sparkling lights showering the sky, barrages of salutes breaking the silence, giant cascading Nishiki Kamuro Golden Willow effect shells, chrysanthemum and peony shells, and red, purple, blue, and amber stars—an endless aerial display of extravagant proportions completely overloading her visual senses.

While not a relevant factor and not the focus of the case, what stuck in Susan's mind was also the fact that Thomas Clemson was a Native American, as was his attorney. Each day, as his attorney was qualifying each psychological examiner, he would ask them questions related to what they knew about Native American history.

The results identified that each of the experts, one by one, initially commented on knowing about Native American culture, which during the course of their being vetted, revealed they knew little, if anything, about it or how it fit or failed to fit into a white man's court of justice. The Native American attorney included direct quotes the experts had offered in their explanations during each of their individual direct examinations. Fair game.

Ninety days later, Susan would receive the Findings of Fact for Thomas Clemson's trial. The judge's opinion was that Thomas did not meet the legal criteria as a sexual predator, requiring a "pattern of sex offenses."

Noteworthy was the fact that Susan was cited as the only examiner, credited with a thorough review of the paperwork related to Thomas's case as a juvenile. His offense as a teenager included that fact that the female victim herself had specifically not identified him as her perpetrator. In fact, she commented about looking directly at Thomas while the other boys were sexually fondling her.

Sometime later, Susan saw a wall print that reminded her of the Clemson case. It was four older male Native Americans, each holding a long gun, standing together with solemn facial expressions. Below the photo was the caption: Homeland Security ... Fighting Terrorism since 1492.

Mr. Clemson would be released on certain conditions that he participate in outpatient substance abuse treatment and AA. In Susan's mind, justice had been served and justice had won. Some cases are worth reliving, and this was one of them.

Chapter 19

The first law enforcement committee meeting met in the lower level of the courthouse. For the foreseeable future, the group would review and discuss local crime issues in Rockford City.

Besides Detective Ken Russell, who was the lead officer heading up the group, and Dr. Kasson, there were several other professionals who had been asked to serve on the investigative task force. Included were a retired law enforcement officer, Vince Martin, who had created and refined an established database for organizing and codifying evidence; a state bureau of criminal investigation officer, John Ward, familiar with similar cases in the state over time; and a retired homicide detective by the name of Phillip Marshall.

The courthouse room was spacious with large tables. Manilla envelopes with each participant's name were lined up on a worktable. The packets contained general contact information for each group member along with their specialty of practice. Listed were the victims of recent and past crimes for which there had been little information or progress, despite extended effort.

Currently noted victims included the names of Milton Beardsley, last seen May 10, as well as his home address, age, weight/height, distinguishing features, and family status.

The same identifying characteristics were noted for Anne Tolbar, the nurse missing from her apartment complex close to the same time of Milton's disappearance. Joan Frye, the name of the woman who lived next to Anne, was also listed along with personal data offered by the police and condo building superintendent.

Also noted were older unsolved cases of missing persons including Anita Mariotti, the ballerina who failed to return after her mother's scheduled funeral, and Elizabeth Nickerson, the missing woman previously employed at the Vela Financial Group.

In each packet was a map of the city, a layout plan of Lake Crest Cemetery, places of employment for each victim, and geographic locations they were known to have frequently visited (churches, exercise centers, etc.). Each victim had been noted with a different colored dot, with the appropriate colored dot placed at the corresponding locations, as supported by the available records or interviews with relatives.

There were lists of career criminals in the area and their present status (parole, recently released, age, health issues, if any, mitigating and complicating information, etc.). Directly across from each point of information was the name of the officer responsible for the data collection and his or her cell phone number.

Also included were details about each of the victims as was available, including interviews with family members or coworkers.

In Milton's case, the committee members received photographs of Milton's car after it had been removed from a river bottom, the contents of the car, Milton's photograph, and a list of cemetery workers with their photos, thumbnail descriptions of their jobs, who they worked with, how long they had been employed, criminal history if it existed, and noted problems, if any. Copies of law enforcement interviews with each cemetery worker when the case was first opened were also included.

Lewis Weller, a lead cemetery employee, was listed last on the list. Some of the comments related to Mr. Weller's interviews noted detectives "not feeling confident regarding the truthfulness of Mr. Weller's responses." They commented about his coming across as "evasive, seemingly acting dumb on purpose, and unhelpful."

Each person introduced themselves and offered a brief statement as to their expectations of the group and what they hoped to add to the process. The formal presentation by the detectives lasted two hours; then the floor was open for questions or comments.

Susan asked if a tour of the cemetery office and crematorium where Milton Beardsley worked for over two decades could be arranged. She also asked if there had been any history of recorded disputes between cemetery workers and Milton.

Another member of the team asked about the history of employment differences at the cemetery and crematorium and questioned the history of criminal activity involving current and or past cemetery employees. Someone asked if the situation in Rockford City stood alone, or if there was information on similar cases elsewhere in the state.

Members were asked to review and take notes in the large three ring binder they were given to review for the next meeting in two days. Susan was informed she could go to the cemetery office to arrange for a crematorium office tour, with other members also indicating interest in joining.

Chapter 20

Susan met the other task force members at the entry of the crematorium as they were preparing for the tour. Several other individuals were joining the tour as well, and recognizing one woman in particular, she approached. "Hi, I'm Susan Kasson, have we met before?" The woman responded with a smile, offered her hand, denied having met Susan in the past, and said her name was Jo Miller, a newspaper reporter.

Jo noted, "This is where one of the cemetery workers, Mr. Beardsley, was employed."

"I know, the tour should be very interesting," responded Susan. "Have you toured a crematorium before?" Jo shook her head in the negative, and both women walked toward the staff member who was about to begin.

The woman standing in front of the group introduced herself, "Good afternoon, my name is Alice Baker. Welcome to Lake Crest Crematorium. I understand that most of you are working on Mr. Beardsley's case. I was made the crematory co-staff director after Mr. Beardsley's disappearance and eventually discovered passing. I worked with him for over twenty years, and I learned much from him about life, death and how to live. We all miss him. I know he would have enjoyed having you visit because Milton put his heart and soul into this place and the people who worked here."

Pointing to a framed photo, she commented, "This is a photo of Milton taken a year ago . . ." She gave a brief history of what Milton had told her about his being given the job in cemetery services decades ago and some of the major changes and improvements that accompanied the growth and expansion of Lake Crest. She explained the tour would proceed in the order of the process the deceased person would go through from start to finish.

She began by explaining the importance of verifying identification of the deceased and reviewed the proper authorization documents for cremation, explaining that some family members requested to press the button starting the cremation process, which fired the flame in the retort. Susan's mind wandered a bit as she thought of the many family therapy sessions she had conducted and the number of people she knew who would also like to press a button to fire up the retorts on a few problem relatives.

"One of the first actions we perform is removing possible mechanical prosthetics such as those containing batteries, preventing 'explosions' during the cremation process. We also remove any jewelry items that the family wishes to keep." Moving on she commented, "Bodies prepared for funerals can be cremated in their wood or metal coffins with the lids removed, or families can choose a heavy cardboard coffin. Rental coffins are also available for cremation."

She added, "If a body is received for cremation absent all the necessary documentation, for instance, if the deceased is indigent, the body is required to be held for twenty-four hours prior to the process to allow for verification of identity. Rules for cremation vary by states. The most complicated processes require more than one funeral staff member needing to sign off on cremation steps to prevent error, the presence of an attending physician-signed death certificate, an on-site medical examiner to inspect the remains if there are questions about the death and verifying documentation, and/or a family member signing for permission.

"The process of cremation can take approximately four hours and results in roughly three to five pounds of cremains; the temperature in the retort reaches 2,000 to 4,000 degrees Fahrenheit. Remains are pulverized for placement in an urn. Here at Lake Crest, we only pulverize remains with family approval. So indigent bodies will be cremated, but the remains are not pulverized until ordered by a designated authority."

Someone in the group asked if DNA could be determined from ashes. Ms. Baker responded, "Even with cremation, one can have DNA testing as long as there are teeth in the ashes or larger bone fragments. DNA sources for comparison can be collected from hair, teeth, or clothes brushes of the deceased."

She added, "Over time, cremation has become more popular than traditional burial. The rates of cremation in Canada have reached approximately 49 percent of the population, 20 percent higher than in the United States. These rates are growing in popularity and anticipated to grow to 74 percent in the next ten years, according to the Cremation Association of North America.

"The cost for cremation can range from $500 to $2,000 depending on extras like rental caskets, funeral service, plot, closing fees, and headstones. Some ashes are buried at the cemetery; others are scattered at sea or other locations designated by the family."

As soon as there was a break in the presentation, Susan asked if the crematorium ever received John Doe bodies for cremation. The response was yes, and Susan's follow-up question was how these bodies were verified. Alice indicated John Does were usually delivered by the police or related personnel. The cause of death arose from various situations, like indigent deaths, nursing home deaths with no remaining family members, or people discovered dead for a variety of reasons not suggesting crime.

Based on the fact that Milton Beardsley disappeared during the first ten days of May and had not yet been found, Susan asked Alice how many bodies had been delivered to the crematorium in early May. Ms. Baker said she would be happy to research that question, adding such information would be on record.

Susan also asked about the process for John Doe remains to be cremated, where the cremains would be held, and what happened to them if they were never identified. The presenter stated there was a specified section of the crematorium for the HOLD /TO BE PICKED UP cremains, adding that some cremains were never picked up and continued to be kept.

Other members asked about the hours at the crematorium, to which Alice replied, "Eight to five, regardless of death happening twenty-four seven." Some wanted to know the training one had to have to work in the crematorium. Others asked about the scheduling of funeral processions along with issues related to funeral protocol.

Toward the end of the tour, Alice Baker stopped at a corner of Milton Beardsley's office, where he had kept his collection of objects retrieved from the retort that survived the heat of cremation. Ms. Baker named each one: a steel hip replacement that Milton reportedly announced he was going to have made into a golf putter, a custom designed fixed wrist for a long-distance biker, metal clips, screws, you name it.

One item, described as Milton's most favorite of all, was a partial metal head cover. She said Milton was a Chevy Chase fan and especially touched by Cousin Eddie, who reportedly had such a plate in his head. Ms. Baker, reached for the metal plate cover, smiled, and adjusted her voice for that of Eddie, remarking, "They had to replace my metal plate with a plastic one! Every time Catherine would rev up the microwave, I'd wet my pants and forget who I was for about half an hour."

The group laughed, and for just that minute, it seemed like Milton Beardsley was alive again and gracing the crematorium with his humor and presence. Surely a portion of his spirit was still present, and all of those crematory employees who worked with him shared and demonstrated their high opinion of their former boss. Some places of work require a special or unique type of levity to lighten the emotional workload of the job. These folks had found theirs.

After the tour, several in the group went to lunch together. The conversation remained on the crematorium. Some participants had read the packet of information and knew that Milton Beardsley was in charge of the crematorium and coordinating the cremation and either pre- or post-funeral arrangements.

Someone commented on Milton probably being the only person who could fill in the details of what had happened to him. Someone else mentioned the fact that it was more than sad for Milton's family that he was still missing. Then, the conversation spilled over into the number of missing people in the area and what, if anything, that could mean.

As the lunch was wrapping up, Susan's cell phone rang. It was Ms. Baker, and she informed Susan that one indigent body had been dropped for cremation May 10, subsequently cremated May 12, which was eight weeks ago, and was still being held for pickup.

Chapter 21

On the drive home after the crematorium tour, Susan's mind was going down all sorts of dark alleyways. Since she had spent three decades conducting criminal evaluations, reading detailed criminal records and long histories of varied degrees of dark behavior, and then talking and interviewing persons of various criminal persuasions, she appreciated being profoundly influenced by this group—some true scoundrels—for her own edification!

She considered the multiple opportunities available to one of a criminal persuasion if working at a crematorium—like an option for permanently covering one's tracks, especially where murder was concerned. Who would ever guess someone would go to such ends? Susan would not be surprised at all. The important takeaway was to learn about these behaviors and who did them without crossing over into their darkness.

Susan knew of individuals who would not hesitate for a minute to embrace any available opportunity to cover their tracks. Hers was a world where people took pride in honing their skills involving revenge, greed, winning at all costs, lying, deceit, and rearranging the facts without a drop of guilt. And these experiences, over time, had conditioned her to recognize/entertain/sense certain "opportunities" that others would not think of—or at least not talk about!

Working at a crematorium could be a virtual gold mine for covering crime; 2,000 degrees for a few hours could drastically impact evidence. Plus, such a thought is creepy, and most normal folks would not even entertain the possibility. But she did not routinely interact with "normal" or even "average" folks. She was familiar with the darkest sides of people and their dark patterns of behavior.

She was eager to read the initial interviews of the crematory employees when Milton went missing. In particular, she wanted to reread the accounts offered by crematorium staff as to how the body of John Doe actually got there. If there was a video system for receiving bodies, she hoped to see it. Also, she considered the fact that much can be gained by re-interviewing certain people on a witness list.

Arriving home, she retrieved the large three ring binder on the investigation, poured herself a glass of wine, got out a fresh manilla tablet for making lists and notetaking, and hunkered down to see if she could find some of the answers—or at least hints of information—she was seeking.

Susan began by rereading the interviews of the crematorium staff and line workers. There were six full-time workers, ranging in work experience from four to fifteen years at Lake Crest. All three of the part-time workers had been there for five years. Each of the two lead staff members had fifteen and twelve years of experience at Lake Crest, respectively.

In the section of the pending cremation checklist, Susan saw paperwork stating that bodies had to be held for the required twenty-four hours prior to being put in the retort, the names of relatives to be contacted, and a list of relatives who reportedly requested to be present when the process began. There were a number of records for each individual being cremated—except for John Doe, whose paperwork was limited and contained many empty spaces and absent pages.

There was also a separate cross reference of each month that listed the cremations conducted as well as a check mark for each of the points in the process having been noted as complete, even down to the exact number of the receptacle in which the ashes had been placed.

Phil Williams, on the Lake Crest staff for twelve years, thirty-eight years of age, was noted as the contact person for the John Doe. Mr. Williams left blank the name of the deceased and checked off entering the John Doe on the list of prospective cremations that would include the twenty-four-hour waiting period. The actual date for receiving the body was May 10—no specific time noted, which was a point of confusion since the crematorium was open from eight to five.

The unsigned-for cardboard container was found in the refrigerated holding room the morning of May 11, with cremation scheduled for May 12. The container was heavy with the body. No one reportedly opened the cardboard coffin to view the deceased.

There were no subsequent notes related to John Doe. No one knew where he died, where he had been found, who found him, or who noted his arrival at Lake Crest. The checklist created to eliminate any doubt or question about a deceased individual was blank.

The signature of the person who filled out the drop-off was illegible. It was additionally unclear how the body of John Doe had been delivered, as there was no listing of this pending drop-off on May 10, nor had it been signed for as being received. No paperwork was available for cross-checking any of this basic data.

Crematorium workers on duty May 10 were listed. Also noted were the actual crematorium staff on May 12, twenty-four hours after the arrival of the John Doe.

Cemetery employees listed during the entire month of May included twenty workers, with each employee's length of service noted. Lewis Weller was listed and noted as having the longest work experience: that of ten years. His background information included his self-reporting a minimal and nonaggressive criminal history during his youth, a factor shared by two other cemetery workers.

If someone had been specifically assigned to John Doe, it was not apparent in the records.

A copy of the telephone call by Phil Williams to Seth Loring was also included, noting concern that the records were incomplete, and no one had picked up the body after two months. No one was found to provide additional clarifying information. Was it, simply stated, just an oversight, or was it something more sinister?

The question that bothered Susan the most was, whose ashes were these? Milton Beardsley was assumed dead. His car had been found without him. Because there was no body, he had a memorial service rather than a funeral. Unknown John Doe ashes had materialized at about the same date as his death. Now what?

Susan was eager for the next meeting to ask Detective Russell if DNA testing of the John Doe ashes were in the master plan, and if so, when the results would be available. She wanted to know whether these ashes were what was left of Milton Beardsley.

Chapter 22

Monday morning, bright and early, Susan left for a competency evaluation at a nearby jail. Her job was to interview Harry Parker, a forty-seven-year-old white male.

He had been charged with Interfering with a 911 Call. The caller was his wife; she was trying to contact police after Harry got out his loaded gun and started shooting at unseen/imaginary people passing by the house.

During his confinement, he assaulted another inmate. He talked about being God, yelled, screamed, pounded on the walls, crowed like a rooster, and spit at staff, requiring that he be sprayed with a riot control agent and placed in restraints until he was under control again.

His psychiatric history included voluntary admission to the state hospital from which he subsequently walked away, against medical advice, less than a week later. He had a history of bipolar affective disorder; his medications at the jail included Depakote, a mood stabilizer, and Zyprexa, a neuroleptic.

The court ordered evaluation was to determine Mr. Parker's ability to understand the criminal proceedings against him and to participate in his defense. An opinion was also requested as to his mental status at the time of the offense, such as his "laboring under such a defect of reasoning as to not know the nature of the act constituting the offense for which he was charged or that it was wrong." Lastly requested was a statement as to the factual basis upon which the diagnosis and opinion were based.

As usual, Susan reviewed Mr. Parker's records including the court complaint, his medical records, his medication management, his contact listings over the past several years, and his most recent state hospital Treatment and Discharge Summary. She also reviewed his medical records at the jail.

She explained to Mr. Parker the reason she was meeting with him and informed him the information she gathered would not be kept confidential and would be put in a report for the court and his attorney. She invited him to ask questions whenever he needed more information. Her interview with Mr. Parker at the jail lasted one hour. Obviously, he was psychotic.

For example, he said he had personally called 911 from the state hospital the same morning as his interview with Susan in order to be of help to his wife. He shared he was the author of several books and that all the books in the jail library were written about him. He stated, "Every station on TV is about me ... the others don't even know the master is with them and worth millions."

When asked if he was having problems with his sleep, he looked at his watch, and when the question was repeated, he again looked at his watch. He denied problems with his appetite and described his concentration as excellent. When asked for a noteworthy news event, he said that his caseworker, with whom he had many disagreements, was wanted by the FBI.

He denied experiencing auditory hallucinations, continued to demonstrate paranoia by looking over his shoulder and around a corner that did not exist, and when asked about his temper, replied, "I am very agitated to know this is going on."

He stated he had medication with him from home at the jail, "Zyprexa for my bipolar disorder … to control my mania … they say I am crazy," followed by laughter. He also stated he was taking Valproic Acid to stabilize him.

He was only able to identify one side effect of Zyprexa, as weight loss. When asked the reason he was prescribed antipsychotic drugs, he stated, "Just to take them … the letters are Zyprexa A to Z … A is for my mother, and Z is for me." He also said his Valproic Acid was "V for violent, my mother's mother."

When asked what might happen to him if he did not take these medications, he responded, "I don't know." He then launched into a rambling discourse about Risperdal (a mood stabilizer) and working with his caseworker to win the ballgame, but in his eyes, it wasn't working.

He denied suicidal ideation or an intention to hurt anyone, volunteering, "I love my wife … I would let the police handle my caseworker."

He continued to offer a pressured opinion, saying, "I don't need ECT because I am not a baby … I have my own job," adding he was born on an Indian reservation. "I'm part Chippewa, one-quarter … they stuck me for a quarter, and I am worth millions."

When asked his biggest problem, he stated, "I should only carry Visa." He reported that his Visa card had been left at the state hospital, and he wanted the hospital shut down for theft. "I ran away to protect my wife. There was a snowstorm, and I hitchhiked to a billiard place and was winning."

He then started to talk about not trusting his wife, saying his wife and his caseworker were involved in some type of collusion against him.

When asked about his mental health history and being at the state hospital, he said, "They say I have bipolar affective disorder, but I don't. Illness is the devil trying to get in your head, and I had to come to jail to get cured … I got cured by Jesus Christ."

When asked, Mr. Parker stated he had been to court before. When asked his current charges, he responded, "Being a good boy and working hard." He denied he had been charged with anything else.

He volunteered he did not currently have an attorney, adding, "I'll represent myself for the crime my caseworker caused my wife … he removed my wife for being a Christian," followed by a rambling unrelated and disjointed story about his father being dead but having given him information in his head, stating, "The key to the deed is at the eagle's." When asked if his attorney would be a public defender or a county attorney, he responded, "The county attorney."

When asked the county attorney's role, he responded, "To catch the bad guys … I want my caseworker in prison." When asked why it would be important for him to tell his attorney the truth, he stated, "Because I am the attorney representing my wife and I." When asked if the county attorney was for or against him, he stated, "He is for me."

Susan asked Mr. Parker about the role of the judge, and he said, "The judge is for me too … he will secure justice for all." When asked how the judge made decisions, he responded, "Because of the findings of facts … he listens to me … I am trying to clean this city up from filth and make it a smoking-free and drinking-free town."

"What pleas might you offer in court?" Susan asked.

At this point, Mr. Parker had difficulty shifting from perseverating about his complaints against his caseworker and stated, "He ain't going to get no plea."

When the question was asked again, he offered, "Guilty and not guilty." Susan then asked what could happen with a plea of guilty, and he reported, "The person will go straight to prison." For a plea of not guilty he reported, "I would be set free … no, he'll lose his job and his license to me." When asked if he knew about a plea of no contest, he quickly responded, "There is no contest with the Parkers."

He defined perjury as "false witnessing … you are falsely accused," followed by a rambling explanation of events that had occurred in his home.

When it came to the meaning of the word "witness," he stated, "I am a witness." When asked the role of a witness, he said, "My wife and I will testify to ongoing problems," adding, "The witness is supposed to tell the whole truth and nothing but the truth."

"Is a witness someone at the alleged incident?"

"Yes," he said.

It was nearly time to wrap up, so Susan asked him how a person should behave in court. He said, "Look straight at the judge, handcuffed and in orange." She asked him when a person should talk in court, and he stated, "Only when the judge asks questions to find the truth."

"What should you do if you hear lies about you in court?" Susan asked.

"They should be put in the jailhouse."

"Who should you inform if you hear lies about you in court?"

"The judge."

When asked to explain his version of the incident causing him to be jailed, his account was disjointed and included delusional beliefs he had about a conspiracy of harm to his wife. He was unable to offer relevant details or information that would be helpful to his attorney in planning his defense.

Susan thanked him for his time and shook his hand before leaving.

She sighed. Mr. Parker had clearly demonstrated that he was incompetent to proceed to trial. His diagnosis was noted as bipolar affective disorder—currently manic—with psychotic features.

The second opinion, related to his mental status at the time of the offense, was based on his demonstrated symptoms of mental illness at the time of his arrest. His noted and vivid perceptual distortions, a symptom of his psychosis, precluded his knowing the nature of his actions or that these actions were wrong. Instead, in his reasoning at the time of the offense, he justified a convoluted belief of a conspiracy between his caseworker, his wife, and possibly others.

Once she returned to her office, Susan would write up the report. It would be immediately sent to the presiding judge, and Mr. Parker would be transferred to a treatment facility until he was deemed safe for release, if in fact he was able to be released at all.

Of course, driving always presented the opportunity for daydreaming and thinking. She was thinking about Milton Beardsley and what might have actually happened to him. She was anxious for the next meeting of the local crime task force. Her curiosity was on overdrive.

Chapter 23

That evening, Susan reviewed records of victims of crime in the local community. Some of these unsolved crimes were dated in the distant past, raising the question as to the complexities associated with keeping the investigations active.

As she scanned the demographics of the oldest case, that of Sarah Nickerson of Vela Financial Group who disappeared ten years prior, she noted with some surprise that Ms. Nickerson had also had a residence at the Terrace Condominium Complex. Of course, this complex was noted both for its security and easy access to the business and shopping district.

Just out of curiosity, she paged ahead to verify the address of the ballerina, Ms. Mariotti, and found that her address was, in fact, not the Terrace complex. Back to the grindstone.

She verified victim names and addresses with the map. Home addresses of victims included a respective colored dot by each name. The colored dot notion was brilliant; she could glance at the whole map and get a better feeling for patterns, or lack thereof. Now that she had her bearings, she compared the women to common places they were known to frequent, like cocktail lounges, theaters, libraries, or malls. None of these similarities seemed to stand out as significant.

Susan was momentarily distracted and intrigued by the personal and briefly noted criminal history for Mr. Weller, the cemetery worker who had been employed at Lake Crest for the past decade. His records noted that he had moved several times to different states, moving to Rockford City from Southern California as an adult, which would be a significant change from the beaches and fast paced lifestyle. The Midwest was known for its winters. It made Susan question his reason for the change of climate and setting. He knew few, if any, people when he moved to the Midwest and was described as keeping to himself.

In his youth, he'd had a few arrests for vandalism and fighting. His adult criminal history was blank. He was single and had no reported family in the area. His history felt as though something had been intentionally left out. Maybe it had been sanitized. Maybe not.

What was behind his long list of short-term and varying jobs into his midthirties, and why was his current cemetery job his longest position of reported employment? He was noted as basically a hard worker. He seemingly was, for the most part, responsible, save for one write-up where Milton questioned as to his being in a different part of the cemetery on a remarkably busy day. Another cemetery staff member had been sent to find him because there were a lot of funerals and no room for screwups.

Why no significant other or close family ties for Mr. Weller—like who to contact if he was in an emergency situation? And what about his history of many moves all over the country? Susan checked his address and noted it was in an older part of the city, close to Lake Crest.

And throughout Susan's review process was the ever-present awareness that people do not always tell the truth. Sometimes there is the initial pack of lies, then revisions of the lies. Sometimes, certain questions prompt more accurate memories. And with the skill of a good interviewer who could feign or demonstrate naïve but sincere confusion and the need for clarification, sometimes people offered more details to fill in the empty spaces, and the real story would begin to emerge.

She reviewed the information available on other cemetery workers. For many, this was a first job based on their young ages, limited work history, and absent training. For some it occupied the majority of their years. It was a strenuous job, not meant for everyone, and then there was the emotional setting of working in a cemetery.

Assessment comments noted fellow employees as "respectful, caring, and helpful." Lake Crest was similar to a family: you got along or did not; you stayed or did not; you did your repetitive job without complaint or did not. Labor intensive jobs require following the rules and pecking order. In general, workers' records noted a responsible crew who had worked together for a long time.

Perhaps these were salt of the earth people who had been born in Rockford City, grew up, went to school, and settled down because they loved the history and beauty of the area. And of course, Lake Crest was a beautiful and impressive place to work.

And there was a lot of work to do at Lake Crest. It was not unusual for students to find steady summer jobs there with good training in landscaping, mowing, and horticulture. Some adults had spent their entire lives working in different areas of the cemetery complex.

As Susan continued to read over background information of Lake Crest employees, she noted little turnover, a sign that people had perhaps found their niche and got along with each other. She also had underestimated the extensive number of varied employees and the numerous garages housing huge equipment necessary for maintaining the cemetery in all seasons. It was a huge and interesting education in a new industry for her.

Chapter 24

The second meeting of the law enforcement task force took place at the beginning of the week. Updated information was shared. Ken Russell asked if anyone had any new information to present or had questions. Susan shared the group's touring the crematorium and asked whether a DNA test could be run on the John Doe ashes, repeating the fact that this body had been dropped off at the crematorium at about the same time as Milton Beardsley's disappearance.

Detective Russell said the DNA testing had been ordered and was in the works. Mouth swabs and hair samples had been collected from blood relatives, and samples had been collected from Milton's toothbrush and hairbrush.

Ken added, "Milton's policy of not pulverizing cremains at the time of cremation will mean that evidence, such as teeth and larger bone parts, should be left in the ashes. Who knew it would be Milton's own planning that would be important at the time of his death? We should have the results in about two weeks."

Ken also reported that new information had surfaced, including the fact that twenty-four-hour video footage of the crematorium delivery door on May 10 was blocked/disabled after hours for one hour according to the computer, with no credible explanation.

Ken continued, "The grounds crew has been interviewed as well as crematorium staff, with no unusual findings as of yet. We have confirmed that the crematorium door lock had been picked to gain entry on May 10. The only personnel present that night included the Lake Crest Funeral Home staff who noted no unusual events but who were also separated from the crematorium by at least a mile."

Staff photos were put up on a screen, and the employees were discussed. No one to date had been flagged with known criminal history. Mostly they got along and shared the work as needed.

Milton's criticism of and work challenges with Chadly, his nephew, were well known and not seen as significant.

When Lewis Weller's face appeared on the screen, he was talked about as a responsible fellow who had yet to call in sick after years of employment. He was seen as smart by his coworkers and on the quiet side. He was not known for socializing with the other cemetery workers after hours.

Collateral information noted Lewis Weller had done intermittent temporary work at the Terrace Condominium Complex, attending to a few tenant's wishes for moving furniture, minor repairs, and carpet cleaning. He had been providing these handyman type services for a number of years.

Lewis did not appear to have a lot of friends, and the ones who he did have were careful about talking to anyone from law enforcement. Each of them minimized or perhaps underreported Lewis's problems. It was easy to see that they had their own histories and knew how to not say too much.

One friend, however, was a woman named Peachy. When asked

if Lewis had any unique skills, she did go off on a rather detailed description of him. She explained that Lewis had a "gift," a comment too important to just brush off.

"Lewis is a master observer, and he remembers details to a tee. He is a manipulator, and he will win what he has his eye on without a doubt. One time, we went out for a beer, and as we sat there at the pub, he started talking about the various pool players. He pointed out one particular fellow and said, 'That player has been watching that game as long as we have been sitting here. He is setting up his next hustle. See how patient he is and how he maneuvers his way into the game and carefully sets up his series of shots? He is smooth; he never gets distracted or loses his focus.'"

When Peachy asked Lewis how he knew what kind of player he wanted to play, Lewis smiled and said, "Look over the players. Watch who does or does not set up their shots. If he rushes in, no planning, no awareness no sense of how he should proceed, he fails to see the order, the succession of his shots, and becomes reckless and vulnerable. His lack of attention makes him an easy mark."

When listening to Lewis describe how much he relished this process of observation paired with patience, she realized this was not just a casual game. It was how he lived.

When other cemetery workers were interviewed, while some of them noted Milton's exasperation with his nephew Chadly, none of them identified problems with Lewis.

If no one had reason to lie, why was some information not forthcoming? The task force would reconvene in four days; perhaps by then, the missing pieces would be identified.

Chapter 25

The following week, DNA testing results of the John Doe body were received, and they were, without question or doubt those of Milton Beardsley.

The new focus became who had killed Milton and why. The purpose of multiple interviews is to get more information to find the killer. On the other hand, people hide information for a variety of reasons, and some facts are never discovered, even in good interviews.

Second interviews began with all cemetery workers in an effort to compare their responses to the first line of questions to pick up differences or inconsistencies. Lewis Weller again did not come across as being on edge, shaken, or cagey. He was not thrown by any of the questions or the reason for a second interview.

When Lewis was asked again about where he was on May 10, the date of Milton's death, Lewis repeated, "I was here at the cemetery all day. I left at approximately 5:45 p.m., picked up some fast food, went home, ate my burger and fries, had a beer or two while watching the ball game on television, and turned in about midnight."

In a relaxed manner, he talked about being a now-and-then handyman for some of the residents at the Terrace Condominium, adding these jobs were not on a regular basis and were also done by others similar to himself with various cleaning and carpentry skills. If he had the time, he liked the additional money.

Lewis described his working relationship with Milton, "We got along really good. We seemed to have the same work ethic. If there was a job to do, we scheduled it, planned it out, and got it done. He was a fair boss. We never had problems."

Detective Russell asked, "How do you think the lock on the crematory door was picked?"

Lewis just shook his head, paused, then replied, "I have no idea how you pick a lock, especially at a crematorium. I would think it would be a real challenge, if it were even possible."

He reported he first found out that the ashes were those of Milton when he heard it on the 6:00 a.m. news. He described his reaction, "I was dumbfounded. Milt was a good guy ... who would want to kill him? We got a great place to work and guys who get along and get things done. He had these long-term friends who went on these fishing trips. A good life ... I can't imagine anyone wanting to kill him!" Lewis then hung his head and wiped his nose and eyes with his handkerchief, saying, "Milton's death was not just losing a boss; it was like losing a friend."

Detective Russell continued, "I understand. Have there ever been any other John Does who turned out to be someone you knew?"

"Not to my knowledge ... this is unbelievable and tragic. I still have trouble taking it in."

"Do you have any idea who would have had a reason to kill Milton?"

"I honestly have no idea. He was a salt of the earth kind of guy. No one should have to get killed like that."

"What do you mean by the phrase, 'like that'?"

Lewis paused, then said, "Getting killed for no apparent reason, taken from his family and his work for no reason. It's terrible. I have known a lot of guys in my life who were true assholes, yet not one of them was killed like this. Milton was no asshole; I can't even imagine who would want him dead."

When invited to consider that Milton might have witnessed something that happened at the cemetery that got him killed, Lewis looked straight ahead and said, "Like what? We come to work early, break our backs digging graves, and work in a setting of loss and sadness. Then one of us dies unexpectedly, and we don't know it for weeks!"

He repeated an hour-by-hour account of his interactions with Milton and the other cemetery workers on the day Milton took off on his vacation.

When asked how he thought Milton's body had gotten to the crematorium, he shook his head and said he had no idea.

"One last question: do you know where Anne Tolbar could be?"

Lewis looked stunned and said, "I have no idea."

All the individuals interviewed were asked who could verify the information they each offered. When Lewis was asked this question he said, "No one but God, I guess. I am divorced. I do not have a girlfriend, no kids at home, no family in the area. I work hard and go to ball games on the weekend or go ride Harleys with some buddies."

When asked if he would be willing to submit to a polygraph, he agreed without hesitation.

Ken ran Lewis Weller's name, license, ID, and social security data through a database that could pick up previous crimes, aliases, or contact with law enforcement. Nothing. He ran a search of Lewis

Weller's past employment history, criminal history—you name it. Again, there was nothing.

Local and surrounding newspapers actively carried the story of Milton Beardsley's discovered death. It was on local and state television. If you did not know the name Milton Beardsley before, you did now. With all information seen as helpful, the public was encouraged to come forth with anything at all.

Obviously, someone was lying. Milton's body being at the crematorium as a John Doe was a ruse that played well.

Police met with the family to gather additional information and to try to determine who might have wanted revenge.

Milton's death was listed as "unsolved" and remained an open file.

Chapter 26

Following Milton's unsolved death, many of the rules changed at Lake Crest. For one, additional lighting was added around the buildings. Also, new lighting was added at the entrance of the crematorium office with photographic capability for anyone approaching and/or leaving the facility.

All bodies accepted for cremation on Saturdays or Sundays were kept in a special refrigerated area. All pending cremations required pre-established calls and established appointments. Everyone entering the crematorium was required to sign in and show their ID.

Motion-sensitive alarms were set up to detect anyone on the grounds near the crematorium during off-hours. If triggered, signals were communicated to police dispatch, who would send an officer to investigate.

Alice Baker's job was changed to that of exclusively managing the crematorium processes, excluding Milton's former practice of also managing cemetery grounds. As such, Alice was the go-to contact person to set up cremations, deal with special situations, and find solutions to problems. As the manager, Alice would provide visual inspection and approval of all paperwork attached to any corpse being dropped and scheduled for cremation.

Lastly, monthly meetings were now coordinated to include Lake Crest staff, crematorium personnel, and security. They were brief and to the point and offered the opportunity to share concerns and or problems as they came up. This instilled a tighter camaraderie among working sectors of the cemetery.

A month later, Lewis Weller quit his job. He told people that Lake Crest was not the same without Milton. He said he wanted to let the office know so they could find a replacement for him but requested that they not tell anyone else ahead of time. He did not give a forwarding address.

And no sooner had Lewis walked out the door than a thick manilla envelope arrived at Seth Loring's office bearing a return address from the State Unit of Criminal Apprehension.

Chapter 27

The letter of introduction explained that an inquest into the death of Anne Tolbar had been ordered by the coroner and supported by the judge due to the suspicious events surrounding her disappearance.

Listed as the contact point for any correspondence was the office of Anne's nephew, the Hon. Mark Tolbar, JD, a state judge known for spearheading investigations into unsolved crimes.

The letter included a synopsis of additional details related to Anne's disappearance. Noted was the fact that her car was seen on garage recording devices in her designated parking spot, absent evidence to support Ms. Tolbar approaching or entering her condominium. Later, her car was found parked and unlocked, stripped of personal items (except her cell phone), and wiped spotless. Photographs of the parked car included what appeared to be vague makings in the dusty floor suggesting a possible scuffle.

Ms. Tolbar's cell phone was found on the front seat of her car, her last attempted call perhaps being to emergency services, as the single number 9 had been entered. Nothing else personal was left. The keys were still in the ignition.

Concern about her welfare became the growing focus of her friends and relatives. They contacted the police for assistance after she failed to keep scheduled social contacts and was unable to be located. None of her usual contacts had heard from her. Nothing in her condominium appeared disturbed. Her calendar noted pending social events and her upcoming work schedule.

Detectives on the case had obtained a copy of the security film showing Ms. Tolbar making the last turn into her parking area, momentarily stopping to speak to an unidentified man who had apparently flagged her down for some unknown reason. The film then ended abruptly.

The figure of the man in the surveillance film was unclear because he was wearing a dark hooded sweatshirt with the hood pulled over his head. Neither the man, his vehicle, nor his license plate were visible to the angle of the recording device.

At 2:30 a.m., the parking garage was described by tenants as "usually quiet except for the sounds of passing traffic."

Another resident also noted as missing on this same night was that of Joan Frye, Anne Tolbar's neighbor. Ms. Frye was also yet to be found or heard from, and her disappearance seen to be of concern. The history of the Terrace Condominium also noted that ten years earlier, another woman had disappeared, Elizabeth Nickerson. She had never been found.

With the passage of time and no evidence of her body being found, Anne's family initiated steps toward a formal investigation.

The ordered inquest followed a review of police reports related to the possibility of nefarious events at the Terrace Condominium. Subsequent and recent determination by the State Unit of Criminal Investigation is that the parking ramp camera had been disabled for several minutes of time, creating a gap in the progression of events in contrast with detailed information in written reports. It was suspected that some unidentified individual had tampered with the video to intentionally confuse what had actually occurred.

Since events paralleling the disappearance of these women included video footage evidencing date and time of the physical assaults and subsequent sabotaging/manipulation of video access, investigators were able to deduce that the two abductions occurred between May 10–12: roughly the same time period as Henri Muller's funeral.

Once the connection was made, the unique challenge was how to proceed in further locating these victims, if in fact this was even possible. A meeting had been scheduled, during which specifics of these issues were to be shared with the Muller Family, their legal representatives, and law enforcement personnel working the missing person cases. The meeting was to be held in ten days, and Seth's presence was requested.

Chapter 28

At the meeting, it was explained that that Mr. Muller's funeral, and the timing of the event included a possible opportunity for at least one of the women to be hidden in the huge copper casket. The National had its own church truck facilitating moving of the heavy burial receptacle without the need for pallbearers who might have questioned the sense of added weight.

While a truly unpleasant thought, nevertheless, the opportunity presenting itself during the same block of time as the Muller funeral was real. Especially since no evidence of either Ms. Tolbar or her neighbor had turned up a shred of evidence pointing in another direction. Had one of the victims been hidden in the National?

All participants sat at full alert, asking questions, and pointedly challenging the idea and notion itself. Discussions ensued, the details of which were addressed. In the end, despite the sadness of the situation and the surprise of such a request, it was agreed a search of the National was the only sure course for the sake of Henri, his family, Anne Tolbar, and her family.

The agreement included assurance that Henri's good name would not be tarnished in any way, regardless of what was or was not found. One of the stipulations was that the press would NOT be notified of Ms. Tolbar's body being located in Henri's crypt, even if the body was verified by forensic assessment, and then only after an approved news release of the newspaper account had been reviewed and agreed upon by Henri's legal team and remaining family.

After all specifications and details were settled, the next step was approved, that of arranging for Henri's casket to be opened, searched, and replaced as soon as possible.

Seth had his work cut out for him.

Chapter 29

Fortunately, because the copper casket was seen as so beautiful, it had been decided by Henri and his family that the coffin should be on view in perpetuity behind thick glass. A glass expert was found who had the experience needed, and with bated breath, he began the process of gaining access to the huge burial unit. Once it was free, it was loaded in a waiting hearse.

The day for opening Henri's crypt arrived and began early in the morning before the sun rose. Two police cars were lined up at the mausoleum, and police officers guarded the entrance. In the hearse, Henri's casket was escorted to the state crime lab where his body was lifted out.

The casket was opened, and the strong and sickening scent of decomposition, barely lessened by the enormous air filtering system, filled the autopsy room. Then, the double-masked veteran pathologists commenced their work. The body in the black rubberized bag was palpable. The bag was lifted out of the coffin onto an examining table. Anne Tolbar had now become a crime scene victim in need of a postmortem examination by a forensic pathologist.

To make sure nothing had been missed, a small hand vacuum was used on the entire National, with minimal results that were bagged, labeled, and sent with the body for analysis. The National, with Henri, was then cleared to be returned to the mausoleum.

At the morgue, multiple photographs and extensive documentation about the state of Anne's body were noted and recorded in detail. Her fingerprints and DNA testing were completed. Despite advanced decomposition, the pathologist was able to plump up Anne's fingerprints with humectant to achieve a nearly full set of prints.

The forensic autopsy procedure was specifically ordered to clarify the cause and manner of death of Anne Tolbar, as it related to the circumstances associated with her sudden disappearance.

The report noted the processes involved, the organs examined, their weight and appearance, a summary report of both an external and internal examination of the body. Of particular note was the apparent damage to her skull in the form of a compound depressed fracture, causing a portion of the skull to be broken in toward the brain.

The conclusion noted was that Anne Tolbar was likely the victim of a brutal assault to the head with a heavy object, perhaps a hammer or a lead pipe, used to accomplish the breaking of the cranium. No defensive wounds, such as broken fingernails, were found.

Chapter 30

An emergency meeting involving Seth Loring, the entire Lake Crest Advisory Board, and four Lake Crest corporate attorneys took place the morning following the postmortem, with Detective Russell presenting what was known about the case involving Anne Tolbar.

Members were shocked, angry, and mortified that such an event had happened to mar the history and image of Lake Crest. The focus of the meeting was on options and damage control blended with sensitivity to the Tolbar family.

Doubly disturbing was the fact that it was now known that the DNA of the John Doe left at the crematorium in early May had been clearly established as that of Milton Beardsley.

Was a serial murderer in the midst of folks connected with Lake Crest Cemetery, or was there a serial murderer in Rockford City proper?

The Lake Crest Board of Directors were horrified that these situations had happened and remained undetected. Frustrating, also, was the fact that there was no clear information as to how the victims had been chosen, or the reason. The eventual newspaper account of Anne Tolbar's murder including carefully worded details, nevertheless made a thunderous impact on the community. The pairing of Milton Beardsley's murder at basically the same time was most unsettling.

Benefactors and people in the entire Rockford City area were stunned with this news. They were also angry that a person capable of such acts was living secretly among them. How could they live in close proximity with such a feign and not suspect even a glimpse of evil?

People temporarily became more alert to their surroundings; the Terrace Condominium became a fortress of sorts. Anne's friends and coworkers grieved her loss. Milton's friends vowed revenge for his death to a ghost they had never imagined.

Chapter 31

Before Lewis Weller drove two days and nights without stopping, except for gas and coffee, he engaged in a number of actions to blur the details of his departed direction.

He told everyone he was heading to New York, including offering a fake address, when actually he was heading west. He sold his Harley for cash and parked a stolen car in long-term parking at the airport. He told his landlord to sell whatever furniture he left behind and give the money to charity or to the next renter. He bought a used car with the cash using a fake ID.

Now four states away from Rockford City, in the midst of intermittent lightning and a few raindrops on the windshield, he looked for a place to stop for dinner. From his experience, he had learned that the best information could be found at a decent bar over a cold beer and a good piece of rare steak.

Pulling into the Corral Hotel Restaurant and Bar, Lewis parked, turned off his car, and walked toward the nearest entrance. Two huge brass longhorn door pulls mounted on massive wooden doors hinted as to what lay within.

The restaurant had an open beam ceiling laden with Navajo blankets. A large and busy horseshoe-shaped bar was located in the center, surrounded by western style dining tables and chairs filled with customers. Some of the music was that of a player piano akin to what one might have found at the Long Branch Saloon. The only thing missing was Miss Kitty, briefly stepping away from Marshall Dillon, extending her hand to greet new customers.

A mouthwatering and prevailing aroma of grilled steak filled the air. Lewis sat two stools away from another man who resembled someone out of a movie set with his cowboy shirt, leather vest, impressive and well-groomed mustache, and a huge shiny belt buckle that no one could miss.

Lewis's initial impression of the man was that he was confident, friendly, and relaxed. Lewis was also surprised at an unexpected fantasy of himself in western wear with, maybe, his own great cowboy boots and hat.

The tanned man greeted Lewis like he was a regular customer.

"Hey, how's it going?" the stranger asked.

"Well, I'll tell you when I figure that out," replied Lewis. "I just arrived."

"Welcome," was the man's response. "You'll enjoy the food here. It's dang tasty, and the beer is always cold."

Lewis returned an agreeable nod. He felt relaxed and comfortable with the stranger next to him. He ordered a beer that arrived in seconds in a huge thick glass mug with beads of condensation already forming on the outside. It made your mouth water just to look at it.

"Are you just passing through?"

"Possibly," Lewis responded, "but there is a chance I might stay. What are some good reasons for living here?"

"Well," said the man, "That depends. First of all, welcome to Twin Forks, gateway to the Wild West. There is plenty of work here, friendly people, and you can make a decent living in a progressive city. If you are looking to be rich, you may need to be in mining or be a really good gambler. What kind of work are you in?"

"Well, I have had a variety of jobs," replied Lewis. "I get bored doing the same thing too long. My last job was just over ten years in landscaping, and I am open to new opportunities, again, something outdoors, like construction or road work. I have also worked in the funeral business. What kind of work are you in?"

The man nodded thanks to the waitress as she placed his salad before him, turned again to Lewis, and said, "I like a man who is versatile and knows what he wants. That's pretty much me, too. I drive truck for Browning Lumber. Have done it for twelve years. I learned to find my way around the city and surrounding areas, and I like my work. I got divorced two years ago, so I live alone. I have two grown kids who have families of their own nearby. I don't see them except for special occasions. What made you choose Twin Forks?"

"Well," mused Lewis, "It looked welcoming coming down the hillside, especially with the storm approaching. I was getting hungry and tired, and this place looked like a good bet. I have lived in big cities and small towns. The small towns are too constricting. I like a place where I can visit nearby attractions and one that has a variety of restaurants and bars."

"Obviously, you have discerning taste," quipped the man. "This is a friendly area, and you can't beat the food here. I have eaten here for three years and have yet to tire of anything. They have homemade pies to die for. The meat is red and lean. The fish is fresh, and they bake all their own bread and rolls. Best bread in the world for toast that I have ever eaten—makes you want to get up in the morning. And I should know, I eat here all the time. Every so often I try some new place, but it's never as good as the Corral."

"That is a commendable recommendation, my friend. You will most likely see me sitting here more times than you will want! My name is Mitch Larrson, with two r's, originally from the Dakotas."

"Nice to meet you, Mitch. My name is Harry Lenord."

Both men finished their meal, had another beer together, and parted ways about 11:00 p.m. Lewis Weller, now known as Mitch Larrson, was tired but relaxed as he walked around the corner of the restaurant to the lobby area of the hotel. He chose the name Larrson and his being from the Dakotas because he assumed anyone checking on his identity would have to run the gauntlet of a few hundred Larsons, Larsens, Larrsens, and so forth in trying to verify his existence.

Tomorrow he would get a local paper, drive around the city, and see what looked interesting. Maybe he would look for a pair of cowboy boots.

Chapter 32

It was the beginning of a new week. After an early breakfast and second cup of coffee, Dr. Susan Kasson planned to be on the road by 7:00 a.m. for the two-hour drive to a state prison to evaluate Mr. Paul Andrews who had been petitioned for indeterminant civil commitment as a sexual predator. Since Mr. Andrews had declined to be interviewed, she would review his many boxes of records to find the information required by the court.

Paul Andrews had completed two past prison sentences for his guilty plea to 2nd Degree Criminal Sexual Conduct and a separate guilty plea to four counts of Possession of Pornographic Works. His pornography record noted nearly 1,800 photos of naked young men and boys, rather than the thirty photos he professed, along with videos of more unidentified juvenile males.

He was incarcerated in the past for sexual assault of a fourteen-year-old male who reported that Mr. Andrews had also sexually assaulted him when he was a younger child. Two other youth reported being shown photos of naked children at Andrews's residence and described Mr. Andrews as asking them to "play" naked games with him in bed, warning them that if anyone found out this was happening, they would be killed.

Victims had reported sexual abuse by Mr. Andrews over several years. For most victims this began when they were ten years old. Susan wondered at times what had occurred in Mr. Andrews life when he was ten that added to his story of offending. In addition to his known victims, there was one mother in the community who reportedly expressed concern that her son had also been victimized by Mr. Andrews, but the boy was too terrified to confirm her hunch.

By the time Mr. Andrews was in his late thirties, six adolescent males from three families had been assaulted. Polaroid photos of the boys had been found in his house. Mr. Andrews had been charged with three counts of 4th Degree Criminal Sexual Conduct (CSC) involving three boys and one count of 2nd Degree CSC related to offenses against one youth. He pled guilty to the 4th Degree CSC involving one boy, and the rest of the charges were dismissed. The court had also stayed an earlier sentence and placed Mr. Andrews on probation with orders for him to complete sex offender treatment and cease contact with young boys. He began grooming most of his victims at their age of ten by showing them good times with campfire sleepovers at his property and sharing his variety of watercraft toys, all-terrain vehicles, and movies, to name a few.

Mr. Andrews violated the conditions of one of his past releases by having several young boys at his home when he was still on probation. The following year, he was discovered as having had sexual contact with a fifteen-year-old male, with the court revoking the stay of imposition of his sentence. Two years later, he was discovered to have two new adolescent males at his home, and he was sent to prison for eighteen months.

When alleged offenses with two charges of sexual misconduct were filed in another nearby district court, the focus on Mr. Andrews intensified. Earlier records had now been discovered showing that he previously completed a nine-month sex offender program following another long-ago conviction. He was also discovered as having carried a former diagnosis of Pedophilia. His then self-assessed future risk was reported as non-existent.

Now, after enough failed chances demonstrating he was safe to be in the community, Mr. Andrews was facing civil commitment as a sexual predator. In other words, depending on the ruling of the court, he would never walk or live freely again in his former, or any new, neighborhood.

He continued to deny a need for sex offender treatment and repeatedly denied that he had a problem with young male sex partners. The fact that his offending patterns had emerged when he was a younger adult and been repeated when he was nearing middle age, despite a history of sanctions, pointed to his high likelihood of re-offense.

Psychological assessment results for Mr. Andrews noted his intelligence as average, a low level of anxiety, and average mood levels. Personality assessment scores noted he had "a tendency to present himself in a favorable light" and that he had a naïve attitude about life's major problems, shortsighted hedonism, and reflected and scattered thinking. When faced with interpersonal tension, there was evidence in his assessment results that he was able to maintain a superficial air of buoyancy, denying any inner disturbing emotions.

Other findings noted he "exhibited a moderate level of psychopathy, lacked impulse control, had an inability to form meaningful relationships, and had a lower ability or sensitivity to experience guilt or alter the course of a particular behavior even when it would or could result in punishment."

Sex offender civil commitment cases are challenging, time consuming, and incredibly poignant. They are also heartrending as details of what actually happened emerge. Such cases require meticulous attention in researching the history to find support, or lack thereof, to the various prongs of the statutory requirements within the legal definitions for this type of civil commitment, which is basically a life sentence. The saddest cases are those when victims testify only to have their perpetrators given another chance at freedom. Sex offenses are truly ugly realities.

On the list of court cases for the day, cases involving sex offenses are simply marked, CONFIDENTIAL. The only people in the courtroom are the judge, his court reporter, one or two other court administrative staff members, the two attorneys (prosecution and defense) and their paralegals, two sheriff's deputies, and two psychologists. Oftentimes, unknown people entering the courtroom will be met by a bailiff asking if they are part of the case.

Sex offenders can be clever and wily. Their outward appearance does not belie the darkness that lives within. As a group, they do not appear physically threatening. They could come from noble professions, like medicine and the clergy; others are businessmen, teachers, and men with both advanced and meager educational backgrounds.

The first required prong to be met in these court cases is "evidence of a course of harmful sexual conduct, defined as that which creates a substantial likelihood of serious physical or emotional harm to another." For Mr. Andrews, this prong was met by his two but similarly sadistic eras of predatory offenses, separated by a brief time in prison, only to repeat his behavior when the opportunity presented itself once again.

A second requirement is that the individual has "manifested a sexual personality or other mental disorder or dysfunction, which was supported by his history and recently updated assessment results. Thirdly, that as a result of these combined characteristics, the individual is highly likely to engage in future acts of harmful sexual conduct."

Some states with sexual predator civil commitments may also add a second designation, that of a sexual psychopathic personality. This is defined as "the existence in any person of emotional instability, or impulsiveness of behavior, or lack of customary standards of good judgment or failure to appreciate the consequences of personal acts, or a combination of any of these conditions which render the person irresponsible for personal conduct with respect to sexual matters, if the person has evidence of a habitual course of misconduct in sexual matters, an utter lack of power to control the person's sexual impulses and, as a result is dangerous to other persons."

While some victims may be called to testify, they can be shielded from seeing or being seen by their perpetrator by a screen placed between them and the defendant, or they may testify in a nearby setting via television. It is a traumatic and often gut-wrenching experience to listen to them share their terrorizing stories of trauma, fear, confusion, and betrayal.

Additional tools exist to measure the identification of dangerousness. Actuarial instruments are used to score an individual related to demographic indicators known to increase risk such as being male, a criminal history, details related to one's history including both sexual and nonsexual violence, the use of a weapon, threats of harm, and noted prolonged suffering of the victims.

Some psychological assessment instruments are exclusively used to determine future risk based on research involving specific groups of offenders and the percentages of these groups that go on to reoffend. Lastly, there are categories that can add to an individual's risk related to sources of stress in their environment, similarities used to heighten acts of violence, and the person's record of sex offender treatment.

Consistently, in such a review and report, it is acknowledged that conclusions are conditional on the limitations of past clinical assessments and archival records, as well as the relative reliability of self-report and third-party reports.

The respondents in these cases usually sit motionless beside their attorneys, listening over several days' time to the accounts of their behaviors. Throughout her career, Susan had yet to see any outward show of demonstrated emotion on the part of any respondent. In some ways, the trial ending their offending was its own relief.

Following Mr. Andrews's case, Susan left the courthouse and began walking to her car, only to realize that the girlfriend of the respondent was following her into the parking lot. She began to yell that Susan did not understand that her boyfriend had been "set up" and was not a sex offender. Susan calmly placed her briefcase in the trunk of her car and informed the woman that she was unable to talk with her at all. Susan knew from reading the records that this was actually her second serious relationship with a sex offender.

Driving home will be a good way to release the pent-up tension, Susan thought. The passing miles and vistas were usually soothing, even if they were familiar.

Chapter 33

Mitch Larrson's first stop was at a leather goods shop where he purchased a fine pair of cowboy boots and a matching hat. When he stood in the middle of the triple mirrors looking at himself, he burst out laughing. He no more looked like his old self, Lewis Weller, than the man in the moon.

He spent the morning driving around the city. He noted the various parks and bustling center with its huge statue of a horse rearing up and carrying a dashing cowboy lifting his hat high over his head with exuberance. He noted the business district with its many office buildings as impressive. One part of town housed a small college and two hospitals. Neatly manicured parks, a small lake with folks relaxing on benches, and kids swinging on swings added to the relaxed aura of Twin Forks. Driving out to the countryside led him to the site of a bourbon distillery, and he stopped for the tour and a bite of lunch.

He also picked up a paper listing housing options in the area. This same community paper noted pending funerals, and in the course of sightseeing, he took a drive around Heaven's Gate Cemetery. This was a much smaller cemetery than Lake Crest, but it was neatly laid out with a variety of pine trees and rock gardens. It was a peaceful setting, just like intended.

He noted the carefully maintained condition of the chapel and main office building and observed a funeral in process by a newly prepared grave. As he drove around, he came across a sign with an arrow pointing to Green Burials. Mitch Larrson had only a paucity of information about this form of burial. Lake Crest, with its more traditional history of sophistication by comparison, had yet to add such an area.

Mitch followed the signs for the Green Burial area and arrived at a peaceful section of the cemetery that simply was a blanket of deeply green grass surrounded by huge pine trees and speckled with a multitude of flat stone markers. A few people, heads bowed, were standing by what appeared to be a gravesite.

Rather than an impressive burial receptacle like Mitch was used to seeing, a coffin-shaped cardboard box rested beside the grave opening. Mitch watched as the family completed what was most likely a prayer for their departed and then all shared in the lowering of the box into the grave. Another person nearest a pile of brown earth began to shovel. Other family members also joined in covering the deceased, now on a journey of eternal rest. Mitch could hear the soft music of a guitar and mourners softly singing an unfamiliar tune. People lingered after the grave was filled in, and flowers were laid on top.

As Mitch drove around this Green Burial area, he came across a section were there were three freshly dug graves. He got out of his car to take a closer look and was surprised to see these were three to four feet deep and obviously hand dug. He also noted that nearby grave markers were flat, slate-like in appearance, and bore only the person's name and two dates, one of birth, the other of their death. All the markers were the same and appeared to be supplied by the cemetery to assure conformity.

"Can I be of help to you?" asked a nearby voice.

Mitch turned to find a young man approaching him and paused. "Good day, I am new to the area and basically visiting this cemetery for the first time. Do you work here?"

"Yes," replied the man. "My name is Glen Baker. Welcome. Are you considering a Green Burial for a family member?"

Mitch scanned the cemetery, smiled, and said, "I used to work at a cemetery, but not like this one. If you have a minute, tell me about Green Burials."

"No problem," responded Glen.

Adjusting his cap, he said "We have had this Green Burial area for nearly fifteen years. It has been well received. Some people, the younger generation and some of the elderly, want a simpler burial experience. They sign up for a space and call us when their family member passes. The family bathes the body at the time of death, wraps it in a shroud, and places it in the burial box, packing dry ice around it for the two days it remains at home. If they want, they can dig their own grave, or if they call us when the person dies, we will dig the grave for them. We supply the cardboard coffin; the family transports the coffin with the body to the cemetery themselves or arranges for us to pick it up. The service is simple but meaningful. The headstones are all the same and list only the person's name and their dates of birth and death."

Looking up, Mitch asked, "How can people dig these graves on their own? That is hard work and seems like it would add to their sadness."

"You are right," responded Glen. "We dig many graves for our guests for that very reason. They can range from two and one-half to four feet deep, which is less than the traditional depth. The overall cost of a Green Burial is about $1,000–4,000, depending on details. That covers the burial and onward maintenance.

"A Green Burial is not meant to last to perpetuity. The burial coffin will decompose naturally with time, just like the un-embalmed body. All will return to dust naturally, so to speak, hence the name Green Burial. There are no additives to keep the body or the grave lasting forever. The headstone will last forever, and some retrieve the headstone and take it home or allow it to become part of our garden area.

"This is all new to me."

"Well, the interest is definitely growing. In the early 2000s, there were only a handful of green funeral providers in the area; now there are over fifty. You can get an idea of the size of our garden area from the top of this hillside. Despite death being as old as life itself, customs are changing as to how people want to remember their family members and also how the people facing death want the end of their life to be celebrated."

"Thanks for teaching me something," said Mitch as he extended his hand to Glen. "Fascinating. By the way, do you have problems with vandalism here at the cemetery? How do you assure security, especially at night? Are there night guards?"

"It's usually quiet here at all times. No problems yet at night, even without guards. The local sheriff or his deputy is supposed to drive by each night. If he does, he has not told us we have grave robbers or visitors past visiting hours."

Mitch, leaned against his car and asked, "Any problems with kids sitting in cars here at night or grounds vandalism?"

"Sometimes, but not on a regular basis."

"How many cemetery staff are there here, Glen?"

"Well, we have twenty men for grave prepping and a backup crew of ten in case we get behind or real busy. There are a dozen funeral homes in the city, so we are busy most of the time. You interested in working here?"

"I could be. I just moved here and am still getting settled. What openings do you have?"

"Well, we need experienced men to dig and fill graves, do mowing, and repair vehicles and equipment. The pay rate depends on experience. What was the name of your past cemetery?"

Not missing a beat, Mitch quickly offered fake names for the cemetery, city, and state where he had worked and lived. He added that he had dug so many graves, he could do it blindfolded, quickly, and accurately—even in tight places.

When Glen asked, "How did you end up here?" Mitch lied again, saying he was passing through after attending a young relative's graduation, was thinking of moving anyway, and the longer he looked around, the more he liked the area.

Mitch thanked Glen for his time, said maybe they would talk again, got back in his car, and continued his tour of the Grounds of Sacred Rest. He noted the main office building within the funeral home complex, then recognized a crematorium. He noted the work garages and repair shops. Overall, he sized the cemetery complex as a top-notch entity. In circling back to the main entrance, he spied a parking area on a hill overlooking Twin Forks and stopped to enjoy the view. He got out of his car and leaned against the front of the vehicle while puffing on a cigar he had saved for just such a moment. *A great new start*, he thought to himself, *really great*.

As the road wound downward toward the city, Mitch decided it was probably beer-thirty and looked for what appeared to be a friendly tavern. It was called the Oasis Bar. Shady parking and lots of cars spoke to the approval of the patrons inside. Western music was playing; the bar area was more than half full. He sat at the curved counter and ordered a dark beer. He looked around as though he expected to see someone he knew and quietly laughed at himself. As usual, the front bar area was active with friendly folk and did not disappoint. Another stranger sitting nearby greeted him like they knew each other. It turned out they were both new to the city and had spent the day looking around, ending up at the Oasis.

Mitch introduced himself, learned the man was a mining consultant newly hired at the local gold mine, and his name was Jake Johns. Mitch commented on his not knowing much about mining and asked if there were jobs available for new hires.

"The local paper always has a list of part-time and full-time openings on Fridays. Check it out. If we run into each other again and I can be of help, I will."

"I'll do that, thanks," responded Mitch. They chatted about the city, what Jake liked about the area, and other places they had called home. Jake also commented that Mitch looked like a longtime local citizen. Mitch chuckled to himself at the successful transformation due to his recent purchase of a fine hat and boots. They parted ways after a second beer, and Mitch headed to the Corral Hotel. Upon arriving, he grabbed a local real estate guide.

He used the hotel's computer to research the area's vandalism, crime, community problems, and front-page local issues including future city planning. Based on an old habit, he also read the obituaries. He scoured the business section, noting new openings and projected growth.

As he educated himself about the area and worked at blending in, he was becoming a part of his new surroundings.

Chapter 34

Mitch learned over his weekend research that the best paying blue collar jobs in the area included precision production, repair work, machine operators and inspectors, equipment cleaners, transportation, and moving occupations. Perhaps a change in jobs could be interesting or more profitable. He scoured the employment news on the web and various newspapers, drove out to the mine for a presentation, and visited a forestry site. None offered the level of income he was used to, at least so far.

After two weeks of not finding the combination of employment he liked and the compensation for such that met his needs, he set up an appointment with the grounds foreman at Heaven's Gate. He reported having worked at various parks, road construction sites, funeral homes, and cemeteries, adding he had extensive training and practice in landscaping, including skills at maintaining and repairing a broad range of landscaping tools and work equipment.

As he was being given a tour of the equipment building, Mitch commented on some of the newer tractor attachments that added to the skill of digging graves in tight places. He also demonstrated familiarity with several other tools, and overall left no question about knowing "his stuff."

The pay at Heaven's Gate was attractive. He could earn a minimum of forty-five to fifty dollars per hour, sometimes more, for training workers, prepping graves, repairing equipment, providing maintenance, moving headstones, and sharpening blades for shrub and tree trimming, to name a few. Mitch also indicated he could be available to fill in on other jobs as needed, such as ushering for larger funerals, providing traffic control, and intermittently serving as added security personnel for funerals where trouble was more than a real possibility.

When asked if his former employer could verify his background, Mitch calmly stated, "I wish that were possible. The problem is, I worked for a cemetery that was privately owned and respected for decades. Eventually it became defunct, with the land sold for other purposes. It was the best cemetery, and now it is just a parcel of land with all the graves moved elsewhere. It had been there for nearly 100 years."

He was hired on the spot to fill the added foreman's position. The person who interviewed him and showed him around said he enjoyed Mitch's alacrity, a needed attribute for working with others and getting things done on time. Before leaving, Mitch walked through the newest equipment building, taking notes and indexing what equipment needed to be checked out in what order and put on a regular cleaning and maintenance schedule. He also asked about training the men in some newer methods of equipment maintenance and storage, which was well received.

On the way back to the Corral Hotel, he received a call that a prospective housing option was available for viewing. The location and layout of what might be his new home was finally ready, as the former renter had moved out and the unit had been professionally cleaned. It was worth the wait.

Mitch now had a clean two-bedroom second floor unit with a small kitchen, two bathrooms, and a west side balcony looking toward the mountains. It was quiet, and neighbors kept to themselves. There was a gas station three blocks away, numerous cafés in the area, and an up-to-date food market known for its meat—and he was just a stone's throw from the Corral Restaurant and Bar. Life was definitely organized again, or so it seemed.

Every so often, Mitch checked the online news in the Rockford City newspaper. He read that Anne Tolbar's body had been found, and the investigation into her death was ongoing. A number of people had been interviewed, but no conclusions had been reached. He decided he needed to keep checking this newspaper for developments, then burst out laughing as though their finding anything related to him would be some kind of miracle.

Apparently, no one had any problem with his current social security number, or if they did, nothing was said. A long time ago, Mitch used the name of a deceased child he saw on a tombstone in the cemetery to get a new social security card, and it had worked well. His fake ID had long listed that same number, now with a new photo of him with his cowboy moustache, longer sideburns, and current address.

Chapter 35

Back in Rockford City, Susan reviewed a consensus from the task force. The group had grown from a handful of professionals to thirty regular attendees.

After the meeting, she drove two hours to the state hospital to assess Steven Booker, a thirty-four-year-old male. The evaluation was ordered to clarify his meeting the statutory criteria for civil commitment as mentally ill. This evaluation would also include an assessment of his competency to consent to neuroleptic medication, which he had discontinued forty-five days earlier.

Susan enjoyed the freedom of driving to new locations and meeting new professionals, and she found her forensic niche challenging and rewarding. The people she interviewed were usually pleasant and their histories of interest. Sometimes they were difficult to engage or keep on track, but overall, she thrived on the responsibility required in these assessments.

Mr. Booker did not disappoint. He had been admitted to the hospital after law enforcement was called to his group home because he was "growling, yelling, and pointing a television remote control at them, stating he was controlling the universe."

His psychiatric history began ten years prior when he was first committed to the state hospital; two years later he would also be civilly committed as chemically dependent. He had lived in a variety of group home settings where he continued to require law enforcement intervention when he discontinued his neuroleptic and exhibited bizarre behavior. He had a long-standing diagnosis of paranoid schizophrenia.

When Susan met him, he was wearing a combination of hospital scrubs and street clothing. He had recently shaved his head after being given an electric razor to trim his beard. He continued to demonstrate being out of touch with reality with his pressured speech, which was unable to be interrupted or redirected. Despite his obvious problems, he denied any difficulty with his mood or thinking.

His responses to questions were illogical, and he perseverated on saying the words, "There is no confidentiality." He declined to be interviewed in the privacy of his room and instead demanded to be interviewed in the hallway of his locked psychiatric unit.

His responses to Susan's questions appeared obstructive, consistent with his clearly not being seen as a credible treatment historian. At one point he reported he was married and had three children; in the next breath he said he would refuse all treatment until he was released from the hospital. His reason for being on the psychiatric unit was because he "had no keys and was wandering to a friend's home." His records reported he had been pounding on the nurses' station window stating, "I'm not getting the supplies I need, like food, medication … there are 120 of me called Booker … did you bring 120 Snickers bars?"

He denied having mental illness. When asked about his memory, he reported, "I don't copy." When Susan asked about his concentration, he simply responded, "It helps to concentrate." As to his recent medication compliance, he reported, "I threw my Zyprexa away in New York City … New York is a dumpster because I was not at home with my wife and kids."

When asked the reason he had been prescribed Zyprexa, he said, "A trucker med for coffee, Snickers, and cigarettes. I take it so I can have coffee, Snickers, and cigarettes." He was asked if he had been prescribed this medication for a mental illness, and he stated, "Never. I threw it in the garbage … I am the sanest motherfucker on the planet … how I feel depends on where I am. I read the news, and I know it is October 14, 1987." When asked if he was aware of any side effects for Zyprexa, he stated, "Not having what you need, and it's garbage … I was over sedated."

Susan asked why he had chosen to stop taking Zyprexa, and he stated, "I can refuse treatment. I feel better when I do because I don't have dry mouth or blurred vision; actually, I like having blurred vision." When asked if his refusing medication might result in his being forced to take it, he stated "Well I would like that too … in fact I will continue to refuse treatment until I am released from the hospital."

In collateral information, Mr. Booker was described as "tangential and bizarre in speech and behavior," prompting his admission to a locked unit. No meaningful medical interview or history could be gathered from him, complicated by his having an extremely elevated glucose level but denying he had been told he had diabetes.

Mostly, records described him as "uncooperative, disorganized, pacing the halls, demanding and labile, walking into other patients' rooms, needing redirection, tapping on windows or hitting the walls, and trying to open security doors."

He would soon be noted as becoming angry and slamming the

nurses' station door, requiring security officers to be called. He continued to offer strange statements, answer inappropriately, and asked for pornographic movies to be brought to his room.

He refused lab testing related to his initially high blood sugar level and said he liked his blood sugar high because staff would rape him if he took insulin to lower it. His mood and behavior continued to be described as labile, and he attempted to kick a female staff member, requiring that he be placed on assault precaution and held in a seclusion room.

Evidence of his substantial likelihood of harm was noted in the fact that police intervention was required to intervene in his bizarre behavior toward his neighbors when he was unable to recognize his actions as threatening. Hospital records at the time of his admission noted him as having been admitted in a state of psychosis, which persisted and remained uncontrolled. Additionally, his current mental state prevented him from obtaining necessary food, shelter, or medical care or being safe to be around others.

As to his capacity to make decisions, Mr. Booker was seen by Dr. Kasson as an incompetent refuser to neuroleptic medication and in need of a substitute decision-maker to protect his rights and get him treated. If he continued to refuse medication to treat his psychosis, Dr. Kasson suggested a petition to authorize his being treated with neuroleptics without his consent.

Clear and convincing evidence supported his meeting both prongs of the statutory criteria for civil commitment as mentally ill. The least restrictive option was that he be involuntarily committed to an available facility until his illness was stabilized and he was seen as safe to return to the community.

Susan told Mr. Booker's treating physician what her recommendations would be and left the hospital for the trip back home. *How confusing it must be to be psychotic and not understand what is happening,* she thought. She knew all too well that it was impossible to reason with someone who was psychotic. The best approach was not to add to their agitation by arguing with them, which only fired up their temper and could potentially result in injury—her injury!

Chapter 36

The evening following Mr. Booker's evaluation, Susan finished reviewing records for an individual who had been interviewed in person by two other psychologists for his pending possible civil commitment as a sexual predator. Susan's role was to review the man's records and write a report that related her opinion as to his meeting the legal criteria for indeterminant civil commitment as a sexual predator.

This man, known as J.B. Smoot, was currently twenty-nine years of age. He was a single male, most recently convicted of three counts of 1st Degree Criminal Sexual Conduct involving two twenty-two-year-old females unknown to him. He forced his way into their home and grabbed one woman by the throat and dragged her into a bedroom, ordering the other woman to follow. He then tore off their clothing, forced them to perform oral sex and other sexual acts, digitally penetrated them, and threatened to kill them with a knife. Both women were held by the backs of their necks, their hair, and arms while they were shoved, pushed, struck with objects, and threatened with additional harm. He took cash from the home and said he would be back.

The assault of these two women followed a previous assault on a fifty-year-old female stranger when he was a teenager and on probation. He entered her apartment through a sliding window, lay beside her bed on the floor, struck her in the face when she awoke, and threatened to kill her if she did not cooperate. He forced her to engage in sexual acts while running a knife over her breasts and stomach, repeatedly claiming he was "mad at the world."

He left and took $800 and prescription medications. He was given an eighty-eight-month sentence.

His history noted juvenile offenses including receiving stolen property and resisting arrest. As an adult, he had been convicted of theft of a motor vehicle, possession of dangerous weapons, carrying a weapon without a permit, traffic offenses, and alcohol intoxication. His records noted he self-reported voyeurism in the process of setting up rapes. He claimed that he became sexually aroused by women displaying fear.

He had been three times terminated from sex offender treatment because of his disrespect of staff and antisocial and aggressive behaviors. He participated in chemical dependency treatment only to be identified as testing positive for cannabis and alcohol. His record included numerous disciplinary infractions, many resulting in segregation. These included making kissing sounds toward female correctional officers and other citations such as disobeying direct orders, interfering with security, contraband, abuse/harassment, theft, threatening others, smuggling, lying, and refusing to work.

He was not interviewed in person, which necessitated a careful review of descriptions of his presentation and behavior by two court ordered psychologists, as well as careful review of his huge number of records. Repeatedly, he minimized his use of chemicals and his aggressive behaviors and denied that he was a sex offender. He shifted blame for his criminal behavior back to treatment providers for their inability to help him. While he claimed remorse, he also claimed that he was a "victim of the system" and demonstrated no insight into his responsibilities for his actions, repeatedly blaming his family, life circumstances, and the fact that no one had taken the time to help him.

His descriptions of his offenses provided little depth and a pattern of changing details, as though he was putting the stories together for the first time. He focused on his losses and "missing the best years of his life" due to others failing him.

Treatment notes indicated a pattern of his appearing to give sincere feedback and confronting others about their behaviors, sitting quietly, looking at the floor during group discussions, offering minimal participation, and displaying uneven progress. He was unable to explain his relapse prevention plan and referred to it as recovery, as though his presence in the program was all that was required.

Past assessments indicated an average/low average intelligence. His noted diagnoses were Sexual Sadism, Alcohol and Cannabis Abuse, Voyeurism and Paraphilia not otherwise specified, as well as Antisocial and Paranoid Personality Disorders. Also noted were blaming others for his problems, repeated acts of violating social norms that failed to cause him distress, reckless behavior, irresponsibility, and lack of concern for others.

He was seen as unable to control his sexual impulses involving strangers in their homes and minimizing, concealing, or underreporting his sexual behaviors. His sex offenses were aggressive and included use of weapons and threats of death. His behavior was meant to terrify victims.

He was seen as highly likely to engage in future acts of harmful sexual conduct since he failed to complete sex offender treatment and was terminated from more than one program. Additional red flags included his victims being strangers, his juvenile history of criminal conduct, early substance abuse, and unchanged risk factors including hostility toward women, an incapacity for relationship stability, lack of concern for others, impulsivity, ongoing anger, and sexual sadism. His history also noted absent cooperation with supervision and his displaying no insight into his risk for re-offense.

His history of assaults noted they were sudden, occurred in the middle of the night, and involved strangers. He failed to remove himself from subsequent opportunities to reoffend, and during treatment efforts, blamed his victims for his actions.

Psychological assessment noted high-risk factors for recidivism including scores noting he was willing to break the law to satisfy his sexual gratification and antisocial orientation. His recidivism risk was measured as high, ranging from thirty-nine to fifty percent, noting a high-risk for undetected crimes consistent with his history.

Based on Susan's evaluation, he was seen as needing a structured and secure treatment setting.

Chapter 37

Two time zones and a lifetime away, Mitch Larrson began his day at 7:30 a.m. He would be training new employees at Heaven's Gate; the group included six newly hired men—neophytes with absolutely no cemetery experience—between the ages of twenty and twenty-five. Mitch thrived on center stage, enjoyed training people, and was good at it. The first order of the day was looking at the daily work schedule.

He paired the men into groups of two, told them which tools would be needed for each job and where they could be found, approximately how long each job should take, possible problems they might encounter, and how to proceed. This was his time to observe who worked efficiently, remembered directions, and got along. At the end of two hours, he demonstrated how to clean the tools and return them to their proper place.

Mitch allowed time for questions; he offered support for people he saw putting forth effort. While personally standoffish or arrogant at times, he was a master at interacting with people, watching them, and listening to how they thought about things.

After lunch, he took the new men through the equipment building, showed them the power tools, went over safety issues for each, and gathered information as to who knew how to operate which tools and who admitted they had no experience. He created a list of men who wanted to learn how to operate different equipment and arranged a time for a demonstration.

Mitch wowed the new crew in demonstrating his ability to dig a grave in less than an hour. He wanted them to see not only how it could be done but also how it was supposed to look. At the end of this packed-full-of-information day, he was pleased that each of the new men thanked him for the time he had taken to teach them about their new job. The day had been invigorating, and Mitch liked that feeling.

He also liked the new hires. It had been a while since he was lead trainer for such a young group of workers. Mostly he liked the fact that they were paying attention to what he was saying, acting like they wanted to learn how to work, and were agreeable to knowing how to do things right.

For a split second, he thought back to his life when he was their age. Estranged from his family, little money, no decent job, and no plan for the next four months, let alone his life. He wanted to go to college but at the time was short on cash. He got a truck driving job to make and save money, then got sidetracked with all the traveling. It was a solitary job, but that agreed with Mitch's nature.

He had always struggled with trusting others, perhaps because of his overbearing, critical father who seemed to take out a suffocating marriage and low paying job on Mitch. That may have been why he steered clear of romantic attachments of his own. Although stubborn, Mitch was a good worker, saved his money, and grew it big time with his prowess at gambling and winning. He had also learned how to resist talking too much or showing his cards. His father once told Mitch he was breviloquent; he looked the word up and agreed. He would say he liked animals more than people to avoid deep conversations about relationships and feelings.

Still, that was better than some of his friends who had perpetually drunk fathers who were mean to them and absent mothers who were busy trying to find what was missing from their own lives, able to offer only a measured amount of comfort due to the barren marital relationship they relived each day. No one got it all; you had to decide what meant the most to you—success, love, riches, safety. Once you knew what you wanted, you had to make the most of it.

If you asked Mitch about his dark side, he would underreport it. If you asked how he could kill, he would say it was the circumstances that offered no other choice. He knew all his vices; he was not proud of them. He had made attempts to change, but the situations he got into were like his shadow, always there, connected to him. He did his best to keep his dark side still and quiet.

Back on the job, something unexpected emerged from the group during lunch. When they were all sitting around eating, some of the men started asking if others had noticed more than the usual number of government-plated cars in town, guessing it could be some kind of law enforcement sweep.

Mitch overheard this discussion, and his ears perked up. He realized he had better pay more attention, like at the Corral Bar where he continued to stop for a beer and visit with Harry Lenord. This had become a weekly custom along with their playing regular rounds of weekend golf and evening poker.

Was his luck running out?

Chapter 38

Funerals are akin to theater. There is a lot to do before the curtain is raised and a fond farewell is extended to the departed.

The next week at Heaven's Gate there was a rush of morning mowing and trimming jobs around the chapel and unloading and placement of additional floral sprays. Graves for the next day needed to be dug early in the morning so as not to ruin the ambience of the afternoon funeral with the sound of mowers and backhoes.

Mitch kept an eye out for new people asking questions at Heaven's Gate. He made one of his new hires his righthand man to field and screen phone calls and messages for irregularities, like someone asking personal information about Mitch.

Funerals increased to weekly counts of one dozen or more, which pleased the stockholders of Heaven's Gate. Mitch had created a surge in respectful inquiries for jobs for cemetery staff, and florists commented on the increased active number of floral orders for services.

The monthly community cemetery journal featured Heaven's Gate as an organized and successful enterprise that grew and served the community well. Numerous photos were included, and training programs for cemetery workers were featured. The stockholders loved everything that was happening.

And then, just when it seemed everything was going so well, things suddenly got complicated.

Chapter 39

The national news the next evening included an announcement that a serial killer possibly originating in Rockford City had disappeared and likely relocated elsewhere. The estate of a wealthy industrialist, namely Henri Muller, was offering a $50,000 cash reward for information leading to the location and arrest of the person of interest. And there splashed on national television was an older photo of Lewis Weller! It had been taken when he was in his early thirties. If you did not know him then, the photo did not resemble him closely now. Still, it was unexpected.

For all his good luck, Mitch had the bad luck of seeing this announcement just when he and some friends were eating dinner at the Corral Restaurant and Bar. When the photograph was displayed, Harry, Mitch's friend exclaimed, "Hey, Mitch, that could be you, if you were better looking," followed by the guys around the table laughing loudly amidst other raunchy jokes.

"On your best day, you couldn't come close to being that good looking, Harry," rebounded Mitch. No one was taking anything about the news report seriously because no one had even a single clue that the main suspect was sitting right there, an arm's reach away. After dinner, the group went to their favorite gambling place for drinks and cards. By night's end, Mitch was $1,500 richer.

When Mitch arrived back at his apartment, he pulled up the news announcement on his laptop. If you had known what Mitch looked like in Rockford City, you would have bet on Mitch for sure. But now he appeared older, and in his estimation, more handsome.

Not wanting to be caught off guard on the job and despite the lateness of the evening, or rather the early start of the new day, Mitch called the answering service at Heaven's Gate and left a message: "I have a family emergency and am needed at home. Both Kevin and Lance are my two backup men in case of an emergency. I am proud of their skills and examples, and you will be in good hands. Unfortunately, I do not know when or if I will be able to return. I apologize for the sudden change of plans."

Then, he grabbed his Go Bag and drove further west.

Chapter 40

The announcement repeated as a top news story, confirming to Mitch that leaving when he did was a good idea. Then there was an hour-long news show that discussed the murders and the suspected murderer in detail, like his being a former cemetery/crematorium employee.

Now nearly a thousand miles from the Corral Restaurant, Heaven's Gate, and what had been his temporary new life, Mitch stopped at a campground to rest. The next morning, he found a gas station that boasted a tasty breakfast, hot showers, and good coffee. Then he hit the road and drove another thousand miles north to where the snow-covered mountains were mesmerizing, and the air was crisp and fresh.

He found a motel with what looked like a good restaurant. He had a beer in the bar and would have enjoyed it more if he had chosen a seat further away from a stranger talking loudly to another person about the police reward. The guy said he would like to know where the killer was, as he could use the $50,000 reward.

Mitch started a conversation with this person, despite suspecting the man was an undercover law enforcement officer. He had observed the man leaning into the window of a patrol car, talking to the officer, and pointing to some paperwork. In his conversation, he went along with talking about the reported serial murderer and asked the man how he thought the police would catch such a person.

"Well, criminals tend to brag too much; they sound like they know it all. Someone will hear him and take him in for questioning."

When Mitch asked if the man had ever talked with a serial killer, he replied, "Too many times to count."

That night, Mitch shaved off the entire middle of his head, making him appear bald and several years older. The next day he drove to a bus depot, parked, and with cash and a fake ID, purchased a one-way ticket to the closest city with an international airport. Upon arrival in Southern California, he looked up an old friend.

Their friendship was long and trusted and one of mutual respect and no questions. A perfect connection for high paying day jobs when one was in special need. Because Mitch cleaned up well and was discreet as well as intelligent, his friend set him up with a temporary job as a limo driver for high-end, out-of-town businessmen, adding he would cover Mitch should someone request a background check.

He drove businessmen to clubs, residential settings, and various office locations, earning nearly $800 per day, not counting tips. In exchange for discreet and impromptu night driving, Mitch's friend put him up in the same hotel where many of his customers stayed.

Despite his cover being adequate for the moment, Mitch had gambled enough to know that luck could end quickly if you stopped paying attention to details or failed to plan ahead.

Chapter 41

Evening news spots continued to periodically mention the pursuit of the suspected serial killer who was still on the loose, dubbing him The Silencer and repeating the $50,000 cash reward. Mitch laughed to himself that he could really use that money.

He actually called one late night radio show host who was taking calls from listeners. When the host queried him as to where he thought such a person might be hiding out, Mitch laughed and said, "Probably an arm's reach away, listening to every word we are saying!"

Lewis Weller, a.k.a. Mitch Larrson, now became Parker Phillips, limousine driver and "fixer" of sorts. One of Parker's new acquaintances was a gentleman from Santiago, Chile. This man, Señor Cristóbal Rojas, was especially observant of Parker's professional presentation, driving skills, and gentlemanly nature that camouflaged what he had learned about his clever and diabolical side.

He approached Parker about possibly returning to Chile to be his personal driver, righthand man, and "problem mitigator." Sr. Rojas explained that his current assistant, Rafael, had accompanied him from Chile. Rafael had been his assistant for an exceptionally long time, but recently, he had been exhibiting questionable behavior, extremely compromising the security of his job and rendering his status unpredictable. He asked Parker if and how he might discreetly eliminate such a problem.

The next evening, hours after work and following a late dinner, Parker slipped a sedative and some poison into Rafael's drink. Seconds later, the man slumped in his chair and lost consciousness. Parker stripped the man of his clothing and jewelry, shrouded him in a clean, unmarked bed sheet, laid him in a rubberized body bag he picked up from a funeral supply store at the hearse rental garage, and placed the bag in the cardboard crematory box he stole from a crisis storage unit address given to him by one of the funeral supply workers for an easy $100 tip.

In an easy-going, unhurried manner, Parker rolled the man into the elevator and unceremoniously to an upscale rental hearse waiting in the hotel parking lot. The necessary paperwork for the cremation had been peeled from a tablet of similar forms and filled out in an illegible manner common to the many other bodies that were part of the added workload caused by the pandemic ravaging the country.

Parker drove the elegant hearse to a nearby crematory and explained he was delivering a private body, which was recommended by the man's son who was a physician. Attendants dutifully unloaded the body and collected the envelope containing the necessary documents of identification, a fake busines card, and two fifty-dollar bills to sweeten the deal. He wished the night workers well, exited the cremation center driveway, and turned on the radio station that played his favorite music.

When Sr. Rojas heard about this caper, he shook Parker Phillips's hand with gusto and told him he was pleased with the planning and execution of his first errand. Both men then completed their packing and headed to the private plane section of the international airport.

When all of the bags had been loaded, the pilot announced that takeoff was imminent. When they were cleared, the plane joined the line of private aircraft readying to leave the airfield, lifted off, and headed south. Parker studied the personal information supplied to him that included his new ID, visa, passport, and a book on how to speak Spanish.

Sr. Rojas repeated his appreciation of Parker's discrete presentation and manner of dealing with people. To Parker, the prospect of relocating to Chile was perfectly timed with his need to disappear. The Chilean wine added to his celebratory mood. Following a savory dinner of Pastel de Choco y Humitas (steamed corn and beef casserole), he and Cristóbal talked at length about Parker's new responsibilities and Sr. Rojas's expectations—one being that Parker would actually live at the Rojas estate so as to be available day or night to assist his boss in any of his endeavors.

As the private jet concluded the flight and descended through the ceiling of clouds, the view of Santiago, a city of about five million Santiaguinos, included distant snow-covered mountains rising over an expansive dark green landscape.

At the Comodoro Arturo Merino Benitez International Airport, the private jet was met by a waiting and chauffeured stretched limousine. The drive through the countryside and city included a view of the Andes mountains and Chilean Coastal Range surrounding the many examples of neoclassical architecture. The car passed an eighteenth-century Metropolitan Cathedral on Plaza de Armas in the colonial core, eventually followed by the vineyards of the Maipo Valley.

The Rojas estate, Parker's new home base, far exceeded his recent domain near the Corral Restaurant and Bar. His new accommodations included a private bedroom with a small living room, complete with a personal bar and an office area. The windows looked out on the swimming pool, which was set against the backdrop of distant mountains.

He ate meals with Sr. Rojas while they planned their day in a dining room that reminded Parker of the one where Queen Elizabeth served her guests. He considered the quality of his daily living situation in Santiago a giant upgrade.

While Parker's current situation was almost too good to be true, he also considered that he was basically a hostage servant to a man who killed people who disappointed him. Likewise, he reflected on the fact that he was living in a country where he did not know the nuances of the language, the customs, or the standard crime payback. More importantly, he saw himself on the end of a short leash held by a master who could become ruthless in the blink of an eye. As such, he began to set aside a stash of money in case of a quickly needed escape.

Chapter 42

Back in Rockford City, Detective Russell had kept abreast of missing persons cases, unsolved murders, and places and locations known to include Lewis Weller, now known as Mitch Larrson. The fact that there was no big news about him as of yet meant only that enough time may not have passed.

Joint efforts involving local and distant law enforcement centers remained diligent. For instance, Detective Russell had been given a copy of the message from a member of Mitch's weekly card group. He stated that he had met someone who looked like the televised photo. Added were the comments of other card players joking about the noted similarities in appearance. Of course, when Mitch disappeared the next day, members of the group began to take their speculation a lot more seriously. Could they have been playing cards and drinking with a real killer?

An investigator went to the Corral Restaurant and Bar, talked to the staff, and showed Mitch's photo. His apartment was searched but had been swept clean. They interviewed his employer and coworkers at the cemetery, but no one had any information. The trail seemed to end and now point nowhere. The killer had disappeared ... again.

Chapter 43

$\mathfrak{F}$ollowing a breakfast of assorted breads, cheeses, cold cuts, juices, and the famous Nestle instant coffee, Sr. Rojas and the dining room staff spoke only Chilean Spanish to each other and to Parker. He took this as a sign that the job had begun in earnest. Speaking fluently in return was the only option.

After the meal, he was given a map of the city, a list of the day's meetings, siesta time, dinner time, and free time. His options, when not asked by Sr. Rojas to sit in on a meeting, were to wait in the limousine parking area with the other drivers or the hotel lobby where there were newspapers from around the world. That first day on the job, the front page of the *Wall Street Journal* included a piece entitled, "Killer Remains on the Loose," and his former names of Lewis Weller and Mitch Larrson.

Oh my god, thought Parker, *what do we have here?* The article listed cities where reported clues had been offered or discovered and the results, which were that the killer remained uncaptured. The cities of the people who contacted law enforcement were listed along with a toll-free number for others who might have something of interest or suspicion to report.

Noted were the familiar names, such as Lake Crest Cemetery and Crematorium, Seth Loring, Detective Russell, Henri Muller, Heaven's Gate Cemetery, and the Corral Restaurant. A brief and fleeting fantasy about calling the number popped into Parker's head. He found it curiously entertaining to be standing around other drivers who were also discussing the fugitive.

When Parker commented that the killer could be anywhere, some of the other drivers scoffed, agreed, or did not act surprised. The variety of obscene methods used by the killer to get and stay lost quickly became the butt of jokes. A text from Sr. Rojas let Parker know that he was ready to be picked up, and Parker headed for the car.

While sitting in the limo in the private area behind the hotel, Parker watched a tour bus arriving. A sign on the bus indicated it was a Rotary group from the very state where Rockford City was located.

Sr. Rojas appeared through the door of the hotel lobby and asked Parker if he would be so kind as to load a few boxes from the bellman's cart into the trunk.

Parker, wearing his sunglasses, chauffeur's uniform, and cap, responded as usual, entering the hallway connected with the chauffer's parking lot. And on the way he passed by none other than Seth Loring of Lake Crest Cemetery who was part of the tour group checking into the hotel for the conference.

For a few seconds they were face to face, and a look of recognition crossed Seth's face. Parker gave a slight nod as the locked door of the nearby hallway magically opened, allowing for his escape. Seth left his place in line and attempted to open the same door, which was now locked. Immediately, another bellman approached Seth to ask if he needed assistance. The bellman explained that the hallway he was attempting to enter was only accessible to vetted employees.

Parker was relieved and thought, *It's a funny thing when you run into someone you are not expecting in an unlikely setting and in the midst of a sea of people, rendering you somewhat oblivious to what just occurred.*

He placed the boxes of files in the limo, took his place in the driver's seat, and turned on the air conditioning. He was deep in thought about what could have been a close call. It was a wake-up call to be more alert. The world was definitely a smaller place; you could run into anyone, anywhere.

Chapter 44

And speaking of new situations, Susan was reading her next case and planning her interview with Bertha Mae Lowell who was a 40-year-old divorced white female residing in a county care home in a small community.

Ms. Lowell had a history of six aliases, all listed, and a noted head injury. Her most recent brush with the law included Unauthorized Use of a Motor Vehicle with the case noted as pending. She drove the vehicle across the state until stopping in a larger community for lunch, where she was apprehended.

Her history also included a past alcohol-related offense and Driving without a License in Colorado, a criminal history in Oklahoma for Receiving Stolen Property, and numerous counts of Theft of a Motor Vehicle, Transporting a Loaded Firearm, Theft, and Escape. Her record noted five past prison sentences.

She also had a history of substance abuse beginning in her early teens including alcohol, heroin, methamphetamines, cannabis, cocaine, and inhalants. At the age of twenty-nine, she was either thrown or jumped from a moving vehicle, sustaining a second brain injury.

She carried diagnoses of dementia secondary to head trauma, poly-substance abuse/dependency, and antisocial and borderline personality characteristics with predominance of antisocial features.

Ms. Lowell had been assessed in a large medical center that offered the opinion she had a "significant personality disorder preceding her head injury" with the statement that it was unclear if her behaviors were solely related to her injuries.

The evaluation order requested she be assessed related to her diagnosis to determine whether she was mentally ill or deficient and if she had the capacity to understand the criminal proceedings against her and participate in her defense (including whether or not she presented an imminent risk of serious danger to another person, was imminently suicidal, or needed emergency intervention).

Additional requests included opinions as to whether or not she would be able to attain competency to proceed, what period of time was expected, and the availability of various types of treatments available for her. Also requested was a statement of the factual basis upon which her diagnosis and opinions were determined.

As usual, Bertha Mae was informed that the interview was voluntary and that the information would be placed in a confidential report for the court.

Bertha Mae's presentation was that of a casually dressed and adequately groomed woman. Her speech was spontaneous and of average pitch and pace. Her expressed thoughts were frequently circumstantial, and there were times when she made statements that appeared to be attention seeking. For example, when Susan asked her date of birth and current age, she said, "Now I am eleven. I'll be twelve on December twentieth." When Susan looked up at her, she corrected herself, adding she was forty-four years of age.

Her concentration for the line of questions and memory for remote and present events were seen as adequate. While at times she would comment on not remembering certain information, she offered specifics to other questions, and Susan described her overall memory as selective.

Susan noted that she was calm and did not demonstrate sadness or despondency, nor did she demonstrate evidence of psychosis. Susan asked, "Have you ever experienced depression or anxiety?"

"Depression only when I can't be with my family, and anxiety when I can't get out of the house because I live with three guys."

Her overall demeanor was cooperative and polite. Her social presentation was that of an individual who was uninhibited and who outwardly could be seen as functioning lower than her formally assessed borderline/low average intelligence.

She was the middle of five children, and her mother had passed away a few years prior. When asked if there was a motto that best described her life growing up, she said, "A rolling stone gathers no moss ... get while the getting is hot." Bertha Mae reported that her role in her family was that of the black sheep.

She reported quitting high school the first week of ninth grade and later getting her GED in prison. She did not remember the exact year this occurred but correctly named the women's prison.

In an odd manner, but consistent with her overall presentation, she described quitting formal education because she had a "teacher who walked like a penguin," quickly imitating the walk. She said her teacher told her to sit in the middle of the floor with Ms. Lowell's response being, "I told her to kiss my ass."

"Could you tell me about any prior employment?" Susan asked.

"Of course. Pumping gas, exotic dancing, waitressing, and

busing dishes." Her most recent employment had been at a sheltered workshop.

She reported three previous marriages and divorces and gave the surnames of each of her husbands, adding one name was "an alias, because he was hiding out from the law."

She expanded on past comments noted in her records related to her past alcohol use, adding she drank "hard liquor and would stay drunk for periods of time." Consistent with this report, she described blackouts, DTs, and one occasion in detox. She reported a "regular use of everything," including cannabis, cocaine, heroin, and inhalants.

She denied remembering what age she first became involved with law enforcement, in which states she had been imprisoned, and any medications that had been prescribed in the past.

"Do you consider yourself impulsive?"

"I don't stop and think before I act; it's not a mind choice."

"Could you describe that?"

"I do not know; it just comes. If I like it, I do it, and if I do not like it, I don't."

"How are you getting along at your residence?"

"I live there because I need structure, so I don't take another car … once I get something in my mind, I go for it."

"Could you please tell me about your health problems?"

"Dislocated vertebrae, spinal degeneration, headaches, muscle spasms. In 1984 they did a frontal lobotomy, which means they take out part of your brain."

When asked about her past court experiences, she stated that going to court was how she got sent to prison. She reported current charges of UUV (Unauthorized Use of a Motor Vehicle), which is a less pejorative response for GTA (Grand Theft Auto). When asked the penalty for such a crime she stated, "Life in prison, and I don't know, it could be a fine."

"What made you mention life in prison?"

Bertha Mae stared blankly straight ahead. "It always gets worse, and I have CRS. I can't remember shit."

"Are your charges serious?"

"Yes, they are felonies."

Despite not remembering her attorney's name, she reported his job was to help her and added that he was a public defender. When asked what she would do if she disagreed with her attorney, she said she would tell him. Susan asked her why it was important to tell her attorney the truth, and she replied, "So he can help me."

She reported that the county attorney's role was to prosecute her, defining the term as "sending me to the hoosegow." Susan asked her what the judge's role was, and she replied, "He weighs the pros and cons of what the prosecuting and defense attorneys present to him … I don't know, I guess all judges are different … he has the power to throw away the key or give me some wing room."

After shaking Bertha Mae's hand and thanking her for her time, Susan finalized the notes for her report. It would state that Ms. Lowell was able to distinguish the difference between right and wrong, with a history noting she did not always care, which is different from a psychotic individual unable to understand the difference.

Chapter 45

Parker followed the detailed daily newspaper account of the Rotary convention in the Santiago Times. He had grown quite proud of his ability to not only speak, but also read and comprehend a second language. When the convention concluded, he breathed a sigh of relief. He also thought about Lake Crest Cemetery and wondered how they were able to get along without him.

Little did he know that the Lake Crest Board of Directors, Detective Russell, and a sea of law enforcement officers also had Lewis Weller on their minds and were far from slowing in their pursuit of him. Nor did the man now known as Parker Phillips realize how close these authorities in the US were to apprehending him.

In fact, Detective Russell had met with Seth Loring after he returned from Chile to inform him that, through the coordination of law enforcement agencies, it had been determined that Lewis Weller had been traced to Santiago, Chile, but his residential address was still unknown.

Before Detective Russell had time to take a breath after this announcement, Seth Loring jumped from his chair and shouted, "I knew I saw that murdering son of a bitch! He was a chauffeur to some rich guy. I never got to talk to him, but I saw him! I didn't say anything because I never got to check it out, but I saw him! He's there!"

The time of this revelation was noted as 9:19 a.m. at Lake Crest Cemetery and Crematorium in the US; it was 10:19 a.m. in Santiago, Chile.

Chapter 46

At 10:19 a.m. in Santiago, Chile, the phone rang at the American Consulate. Although Parker had not yet been arrested, information about the process of extradition was requested.

In such cases, lawyers could be helpful, if not absolutely necessary. Some countries refused extradition if the suspect's crime was not considered a crime in the home country. Other reasons for not supporting extradition would include one country torturing prisoners or using the death penalty. Murder, as a serious life-ending crime, was unlikely to be blocked for extradition, but there were always exceptions.

Problems could occur when crimes included individuals involved in military, political offenses, or violent acts, none of which were the case for Lewis Weller a.k.a. Parker Phillips. The biggest immediate challenge would be locating his residential address and successfully apprehending him.

The cost of extradition could vary, between several hundred dollars to over $2,000 per extradition. Because Henri Muller's estate was involved, the cost would not be a problem, and Mr. Muller's history of good deeds for others would be seen as continuing long after his death. This man had done much for Rockford City; now it was time to step up and repay his generosity.

Parker Phillips was first informed of the situation by a well-placed, undercover contact person planted in the embassy by Sr. Rojas. The undercover plant informed Sr. Rojas when Lewis Weller's name entered the computer system. Also included was a photo ID.

When Cristóbal and Parker looked at the file photo, they both burst out laughing. Sr. Rojas kidded Parker that he looked better as Parker Phillips than Lewis Weller, which could not have been further from the truth, as he now looked much older. Most interesting was the fact that there had been no known calls to the authorities flagging interest in Parker.

Sr. Rojas had not known about Parker's history as a cemetery and crematorium worker and said such skills were very useful, adding he had friends with funeral home connections who might be interested in knowing Parker better. Rojas was especially fascinated with the fact that someone had been cremated by mistake. He jokingly added that perhaps he should have the staff watch Parker more closely for Cristóbal's own safety.

A serious discussion ensued about staging Parker's disappearance so as to divert attention in another direction, thus allowing Parker to continue as Sr. Rojas's righthand man and driver. Parker asked if a bounty had been placed on his head, which would make it advantageous for Cristóbal to turn him in. They sat together talking and drinking expensive scotch, which added to the festive occasion, and laughing at their combined levels of cleverness. Both men retired to bed at 1:30 a.m.

Chapter 47

Early the following morning, Parker awoke, showered, went downstairs for breakfast, and asked the garage man to wash the limo and have it ready by 9:00 a.m. He read the morning paper, dressed in his chauffer's uniform, and went to the limo, which was parked under the portico nearest the residence. It was a perfect day, somewhat cool without clouds or wind. He stood beside the car waiting for Sr. Rojas.

Parker knew he was at an impasse. He needed to get out of Chile. Based on what he had learned about Sr. Rojas's business enterprises, it was unlikely that his boss would just agree with his leaving, let alone help him leave. After all, Parker now knew too much. However, there were people who would benefit from the demise of the Rojas enterprise. One person in particular was eager to fund and facilitate Parker's leaving Chile in exchange for the elimination of Sr. Rojas.

That evening, during a marathon drinking spree, Parker placed a lethal sedative in one of Cristóbal's last drinks. A short time later, he assisted him into the elevator and to his bedroom. He helped him into bed. Then Parker went to his own bedroom and fell fast asleep.

The next morning, Parker had a cup of coffee while seemingly waiting for Sr. Rojas. He continued with his usual morning routine of gathering the most recent newspapers for his boss to read on the drive, checked the weather, and reviewed the map to their next destination.

While waiting by the limousine, an ambulance siren could be heard approaching, only to actually enter the Rojas estate. Parker ran to the front door of the residence.

"What is happening? Why is the ambulance here? Where is Sr. Rojas?"

The three house servants were all in tears. Cristóbal's main servant was trying to comfort the women despite being personally distraught himself.

They reported that Sr. Rojas did not come downstairs as usual that morning, and when his butler checked on him, he was not breathing and appeared to have expired during the night. Parker immediately shared that he and Cristóbal had consumed several glasses of alcohol into the early hours of the morning, and both of them rode the elevator together. He appeared shaken at the news of the death and wanted to know more details, which were not available.

Sr. Rojas's personal physician arrived soon and confirmed the death. The staff were in a varied state of disorder. Parker, despite his history of being familiar with death and dying, put on his best look of surprised despair and paced in a circle in response to the horrible and sad news.

The physician asked what they drank and the amounts. He said the death appeared peaceful and that Cristóbal had simply expired during the course of the night with no evidence of distress.

Sr. Rojas had left a long-standing request with his physician that, if and when he died, he wanted a private service and to be buried in the property's cemetery with his beloved pets. He had left letters of appreciation and various amounts of cash for each of his staff.

The funeral service took place the next day.

Chapter 48

The evening after Sr. Rojas's funeral, with credit to underground assistance, Parker secured a new passport, three credit cards, other incidental but possibly necessary forms of identification, and a one-way plane ticket to Lyon, France. His final destination would be in the mountains and wooded hillsides of La Besseyre-Saint-Mary, north and west of Marseille, not far from the Mediterranean Sea.

This was the birthplace of his mother and the setting of the many stories she told him over and over as a child about her homeland. His favorite was a legend about the Beast of Gevaudan. It was a vivid and terrifying tale of mayhem, as the Beast killed over 100 people including men, women, and children between 1764–1767.

As a child, the first few times he listened to the stories of the creature, he was both fascinated and terrified. He asked his mother how such a terrible story might be true, and each time she affirmed it was, in fact, completely true. He had also voiced concern and confusion as to his being related in some way to the Beast, as he was fearless in the face of harm.

He also recognized that he had a conscience that differed from his peers and caretakers, and he was aware of his penchant to be able to tell convincing lies. He ultimately made peace with his long familiar and darker nature and learned how to make it work for him.

Most captivating was his memory of the many stories his mother would share with him about the Beast attacking others, including a ten-year-old boy and a group of seven similar-aged friends. The children supposedly drove the creature off with sticks and were rewarded by King Lewis XV. One of the boys who led the fight earned a free education—paid for by the king himself.

A large bounty was attached to the creature's head, and the story of the Beast was told from Brussels to Boston. It was actually known as one of history's first media sensations.

There were also times when young Lewis asked his mother if killers still existed and were personally untouched by their acts of violence. She could never fully understand or completely assuage his endless concern and angst as to whether one could engage in such acts and not feel anything. The boy repeated his thoughts, and they became his nearly constant companion. He was unable to make peace with his personal obsession with the legend, which he often declined to discuss with anyone but his mother. As a child he was sensitive to how people reacted to such information and was able to add untruths when necessary.

His constant debate with himself was, *How did I get to be like this?* which centered around his inability to feel remorse. He understood he was different from others, especially when it came to empathy and conscience, but was unable to find ways to actually change the way he felt; nothing worked.

He was not a child who had been exposed to violence in his home, but he had seen violence on television and in the news. Sometimes, he honestly did recognize the suffering of others, but in other instances, he saw himself as numb to the level of violence in a situation. Worse yet were the times when he felt numb to intervene. *Perhaps,* he reasoned, *this was because violence has more than doubled since the 1950s, and gun violence has tripled since 1985.* To him this meant that violence was indeed increasing, was real, and was clearly not his problem.

He actually read books about differences in empathy and conscience in children and how these levels can shift or become worse, depending on the settings and circumstances. He took pride in knowing he had never been cruel to animals, thereby distancing himself from the usual list of personality features of criminals purported by psychologists. But he knew some would say he was cruel to humans.

He could honestly say that he had accepted violence as a way to solve certain problems despite the fact that he knew this made no sense. He had considered and debated these beliefs for years, but never was there any peaceful resolve.

Now packed and ready to depart from Chile, before God forbid his being discovered and returned to the Lake Crest fray in the States, he called a taxi to take him to the Santiago airport. During the taxi ride, he looked longingly at the Spanish architecture, knowing he most likely would not be back to this wonderful place anytime soon—if ever.

As the plane took off, he watched the terrain below become smaller, fade, and finally disappear. He hoped, at least on some level, he could make a home for himself, perhaps in the French hillsides.

At times he longed for a more peaceful existence. History however, had made such a reality only a pipe dream, and he knew personal chaos had never been completely detached from his life. He also knew that when life became too ordinary, he became restless.

Chapter 49

Back in the States, Susan was driving home after another forensic evaluation when she heard the radio announcement: Lewis Weller had been located in Chile. The interruption of the usual programming noted that, while Lewis Weller's long undisclosed location had been discovered, he disappeared prior to being apprehended. Phone numbers were offered to the public in case someone, somewhere, had new information to add to the case.

Again, the issue seemingly had become: who was most clever? The person being pursued, or the people in pursuit of the one on the lam? It was a story as old as time, balancing the succession of events, existing opportunities, degrees of cleverness, and the influence of Lady Luck herself.

And Lewis had a history of being lucky. Sometimes it seemed like it was part of the mosaic of his personality constellation for whatever reason, possibly related to his skill at planning, timing, and being clever.

Chapter 50

The newspaper account of Lewis's travels and suspected additional murders distracted Susan from thoughts of her most recent forensic assessment of a woman who was, herself a sex offender, which is a somewhat uncommon but not unheard-of situation. Women were typically more involved in recruiting and coaxing victims into dangerous situations and/or providing a false sense of safety.

The newscaster's description of Lewis reminded Susan of the human nature to trust the best in others, to the exclusion of conflicting information such as psychopathy. She thought back to her own cognitive dissonance in the course of her training and in her practice. This resulted in recognizing psychopathic traits, not only in the criminals she evaluated but at times, seemingly evident in other supposedly ordinary people.

She was hoping to compare notes with Detective Ken Russell on Lewis Weller's ability to once again slip through the system.

Chapter 51

And a world away, Lewis Weller's plane was now landing at the Lyon-Saint-Exupery International Airport. When not sleeping, he had spent time considering how he planned to make his new location in Lyon successful.

As was his custom in moving to a new city, he began by finding a pub where he could get a cold beer and information about where to find work and a modest place to live.

He considered a delivery job with GPS being a great way to get familiar with a new area. The bigger question was, how to immerse himself in his new home and not get sidetracked ... again.

He contemplated working in a school as a custodian. A respected and necessary job, polishing floors, cleaning classrooms, getting in on the local gossip. He was also comfortable, if not numb, to working around loss, death, and sadness without feeling sad. He could always find a funeral home or hospital morgue that needed help. And in some strange way, his sense of calm in such settings was somehow stabilizing to those in the depths and chaos of sadness and loss.

He realized that despite all his darkness, he was a good worker, helpful to his workmates, and responsible. His lack of compassion in the face of loss was only apparent to him when he was around others who were struggling from their personal inner sadness. In reality, he felt nothing.

Others' level of sadness was beyond his reach, so far beyond that he could not even fake it. These were his private thoughts when he was alone and reflecting on his life. He compared himself with others, hoping for some kind of new insight, while at the same time not wanting to give up his true sense of complacency.

Chapter 52

Susan was sitting at a stoplight on her drive to a local hospital psychiatric unit for an interview with a man named Matthew Thomas who had been admitted over the weekend. She watched with amusement as a woman tried to catch her black lab, who was managing to stay just far enough in front of the race to avoid being caught. The dog seemed to have an uncanny sense of the right amount of time to spend sniffing bushes before running off in a new direction.

Susan identified with the owner's frustration of her dog being in charge instead of her, the supposedly higher order human. One of life's lessons ... put the leash on before letting the dog out for the morning walk, which made her wonder, do dogs gloat when they have their humans over a barrel? Do they plan these antics? Who cares? We quickly and easily resume loving them.

The early morning atmosphere gracing the hospital grounds was peaceful and fresh. It had rained overnight, and the shrubbery was dotted with drops of dew. Gardenia bushes had huge blooms, and their fragrance permeated the air. Susan entered the building, and the electronic doors opened ahead of her like Moses parting the sea.

She took an elevator to the seventh-floor psych unit. The fragrance of freshly brewed coffee laced the air and mixed with the sound of the morning newscasts on nearby televisions. Support staff were busy delivering breakfast trays, and the medical staff were clustered at the main desk areas or in visible windowed meeting rooms, reviewing staff change information for the day.

Susan found her patient's chart and sat down to review the admission history, medication list, and the recent nurse's notes. The patient was a white male, thirty-one years of age. Her eyes scanned wording and descriptions that laid the groundwork for understanding the man she was about to interview. Mental illness issues had become apparent in his late teens and early twenties, ultimately determined as a schizoaffective disorder. This can be a difficult diagnosis to make due to the interaction/presence of symptoms of both psychosis and mood disturbance, possibly additionally influenced by episodic or regular substance use.

Typically, the presence of delusions and/or hallucinations rather than mood symptoms are more prominent in schizoaffective disorder compared with schizophrenia, in which patients display a more muted presentation. However, the proportion of mood to psychotic symptoms may change over time, and the diagnosis may also be changed. This would be a factor in Mr. Thomas's history.

He had been treated with Zyprexa, a neuroleptic. As this medication reduces the psychosis, it can also cause uncontrollable tremors, dry mouth, blurred vision, and sedation. As a result, patients tend to stop taking their medication, and within a short period of time, demonstrate the retuning symptoms of psychosis. This sets up a vicious cycle, contributes to changes in both mood and thinking, and creates a revolving door of psychiatric care.

Matt's chart noted he had discontinued his medication forty-five days prior to his admission; he also had a history of alcohol abuse. His behaviors prior to hospitalization included yelling obscenities to people on the street from a third story window at his group home along with mounting agitation, inability to sleep, delusional comments about others taking his property and talking about him behind his back, reportedly hearing voices specifically directed at him from the television (even when it wasn't on), making growling sounds in the presence of others, yelling threats to seen and unseen persons, and pointing a television remote control at others stating he was going to "control the world and then destroy it." He also had threatened to hurt people for speaking badly about him when in fact, they had not said a word.

Ultimately the police were called. Matt was taken to the hospital where he repeatedly slammed the half-door at the nurses' station or sat blankly staring into space. When spoken to, he voiced threats of sexual acts and demanded pornographic movies. He was given emergency medication to control his agitated state and ultimately placed in seclusion when he was unresponsive to redirection and persisted in threats of harm to both patients and staff.

"Good morning, Matt. My name is Dr. Kasson. I have been asked to visit with you to perhaps find a solution for your problems." Matt was curled up in his bed. He raised his head and slowly sat up.

"What can you tell me about how it is you ended up here, Matt? What is going on?"

"Nothing's going on … I was taking my meds … there is no confidentiality … I was trying to get a part-time job, but I knew they didn't like me … my meds make me worse, so I quit them … I was getting better when … the police showed up at my door. This is all bogus, what they need to do is get rid of all these birds flying around everywhere in this place ... you can hear their wings flapping from here ... soon they will be shitting all over everything ... I need to get out of here, people are crazy here ... they said I had to go with them."

Susan leaned against the wall; Matt continued talking. "It's nuts. They took me away like in a movie, forced me into a cage in their car, and then told lies about me ... it was surreal ... no one was standing up for me anywhere, just blaming me ... even the government was blaming me and now you are here ... I am trying to control the universe ... people do not like my power or my looks ... it is the same government control shit I have been through before ... I am being poisoned ... I am held like a prisoner ... people want to keep me from controlling the world ... they don't know what's coming."

Susan remained about eight feet away from Matt, and support staff flanked her. In a soft voice Susan said, "What seems like it would be most help for you, Matt?" to which he responded, "I am fine. I can see ... people keep lying about me and trying to force me to do things."

"What are some examples of that, Matt?"

"Well, they want me to see the new psychiatrist, but I know him to be an evil man ... he treats all of us, and none of us get better ... I don't want anything to do with him. He has a tattoo on his arm that is the mark of Satan. I saw it, and when I asked about it ... he lied and said it was just a design. ... He didn't think I knew the difference."

"Have you been in this hospital before Matt? Have you . . ." And before she could finish asking the question, he began banging on his head with his fists. "Yes, yes, yes ... nothing helps except turning on the television ... I need to feel the waves in the air ... you cannot see them, but the power is in their presence."

Susan shifted and asked, "What has been most helpful for you in managing your illness?"

"There is nothing wrong with my mind! I think more clearly than others. ... They suspect me as being a wizard for that reason. ... There is nothing I can do for their delusions about me. ... I know my rights. ... I can refuse treatment. ... The pills they force me to take make me have blurred vision ... but I can still see the blurred spirits. ... I will refuse meds until I am given back my rights."

When asked if he had any physical health problems that caused him concern, he acknowledged having diabetes, then added "The insulin they ask me to take makes me have diabetes. ... They don't want people to know that ... the insulin keeps you having diabetes ... I quit it, and I know if I took it again, the staff would rape me."

Susan softly commented on how it must be tiring to have so much to think about, and what did he need most.

"Nothing ... there is nothing wrong with me! ... These people need the help, not me!"

She thanked Matt for his time and exited the room.

Clearly Matt met criteria for civil commitment defined as evidencing a "substantial psychiatric disorder ... which grossly impairs judgment, behavior, capacity to recognize reality or to reason ... with disturbed behavior ... posing a substantial likelihood of physical harm to self or others."

He also demonstrated lacking the capacity to make decisions related to his treatment in his lack of awareness of his situation, need for neuroleptic medication, and the ability to make a reasoned choice for treatment not based on delusions.

Susan returned to her office and dictated her report; Matt's court hearing would be in one week. The judge would most likely order his hospitalization for treatment, and he would be back in his group residence or other setting in one to two months.

Matt, unfortunately, was an individual within the mass of the mentally ill whose need for treatment would keep him in a perpetual revolving door of relapse and at least partial stabilization. He could help himself by getting involved in a good aftercare group, but he was not yet of that mindset.

Chapter 53

In Rockford City, autumn was in the air. The leaves were starting to change colors, and school buses were back in the stream of traffic. At Lake Crest there continued to be a steady stream of souls who had completed their earthly journey mixed among the young staff who were still learning what life lessons existed and which were most important. Lake Crest remained a place of enduring rest and peace.

On this day, huge sprays of mums and roses stood on display in large floral arrangements awaiting the services for their honored guests. Cars entered the parking area; people walked slowly and solemnly to the respective chapels to say their goodbyes. Families clustered together for support; individuals stood in line for the chapel areas where friends and family honor their loved one.

The pomp and circumstance of the services remained always respectful. Even the walkways crowded with guests and family members on their way to attend such services included airs of respect and solemnity. Funerals were like that: celebrations of life reflecting the lives of the deceased individuals.

One could step out on the patio at Lake Crest and look out over the vast expanse of gravestones, some still resplendent with floral wreaths from a recent service. Entire hillsides surrounding the area were dotted with graves from more than one hundred years, some long bare as family members themselves departed.

Detective Russell gazed at this vast sea of gravestones contemplating its history of benevolent care, along with the dark and twisted secrets it held, unknown to the public and shared only with other members of law enforcement and professionals within the funeral profession.

Perhaps the fact that at least one grave shared space with a total stranger, like the story of Henri Muller's large, solid copper casket, was not as unlikely as one might think.

Death was not new, nor the customs of celebrating life's end. Were there other yet unknown, or never to be known, secrets in this beautiful and manicured expanse?

Considering that the number of missing persons exceeded the number of actually discovered bodies, such people could be just about anywhere. Beyond the most distant hillside was the seemingly endless open sky, the onward and unstoppable passing of time … and opportunity.

While pondering these random thoughts, Ken was momentarily distracted by the vibration of his cell phone in his jacket pocket.

Reaching for the phone, he thought to himself, "Now what?"

Stay tuned.

About the Author

D r. Rosemary Linderman has practiced as a forensic psychologist for three decades. Following completion of her clinical psychology doctoral degree, she completed a twelve-month forensic psychology internship at Florida State Hospital in Chattahoochee, Florida, preceded by training periods at a Federal Medical Center prison, a community mental health center, and a diagnostic internship at a chemical dependency treatment facility.

Her training has included assessment of mental status, orientation, and competency issues related to ability to stand trial, offer a plea, consent to taking or refusing neuroleptic medication, Electro Convulsive Treatment, mental status at the time of the offense, criminal responsibility issues, determination of insanity, capacity to make treatment decisions, and the identification of certain individuals as dangerous.

Her first book, *Grains of Truth: Grains of Deceit,* was published in 2018 and is the true story of a man civilly committed as Mentally Ill and Dangerous to a state hospital for twenty-three years until finally released.

No part of any book written by Dr. Linderman may be copied or shared without her permission.

Contact Rose at roselinderman@yahoo.com